Questions, Answers & Explanations

EASA PPL Revision Papers

Flight Performance & Planning

Written and illustrated by
Helena B A Hughes

POOLEYS
Air Pilot Publishing

STOP PRESS – New UK CAA PPL e-Exams - The UK CAA are introducing new PPL e-Exams from October 2020. Rather than using paper exam sets, all the exams will now be taken online under controlled conditions. They will, however, still be taken at your flying school and under the supervision of an approved individual. Please note that the syllabus has not changed. By reading the Air Pilots Manuals and other reading materials mentioned in the books, and by testing yourself with the following test papers, you will be ready to undertake these new exams. The CAA has issued guidance for students taking these exams and this can be found by searching online for CAP1903G.

Copyright © 2020 Pooleys Flight Equipment Limited.

EASA Private Pilot Licence Aeroplane Questions, Answers & Explanations – Flight Performance & Planning

ISBN 978-1-84336-204-3

First Edition published February 2014
Reprinted June 2014
Reprinted February 2016
Reprinted January 2017
Revised Edition July 2017
Revised Edition September 2020

Origination by Pooleys Flight Equipment Limited.

Published by Pooleys Flight Equipment Ltd

Elstree Aerodrome
Hertfordshire WD6 3AW
Tel: +44(0)20 8953 4870
Web: www.pooleys.com
Email: sales@pooleys.com

AUTHOR

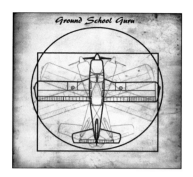

Helena B A Hughes

Helena Hughes was born into an aviation household, having her first informal "flying lesson" at the age of four. Her late father David was a flying instructor and also flew corporate jets. On leaving University Helena obtained her PPL. Shortly afterwards she started work in Air Traffic Control at London Luton Airport earning her Controllers Licence in 1990. Helena continues to be an operational Air Traffic Control Officer and is currently posted to Swanwick working "Thames Radar", "Luton Radar" and "Heathrow Special"; she is involved in controller training as both an Instructor and Assessor. Helena holds a fixed wing CPL/IR and has been a flying instructor since 1996. She also holds a PPL(H) and is a Radio Telephony and Air/Ground Examiner.

Helena would like to thank: Mrs. Brenda "Bedda" Hughes; Mr. Andrew Temple of Solent Flight Ltd; A Vrancken and H Ewing

INTRODUCTION

This book is intended as an aid to revision and examination preparation for those studying for the grant of an EASA PPL. Ideally its use should follow a period of self or directed study to consolidate the knowledge acquired and identify any areas of weakness prior to attempting the PPL examinations themselves.

The questions and answers in this publication are designed to reflect those appearing in the current examination papers and are set out in a representative format. No attempt has been made to replicate any actual examination paper.

Blank answer sheets are provided at the end of the book which may be photocopied to enable multiple attempts at each exam.

EDITORS

Dorothy Saul-Pooley LLB(Hons) FRAeS

Dorothy holds an ATPL (A) and a CPL (H), and is both an instructor and examiner on aeroplanes and an instructor on helicopters. She is Head of Training for a school dedicated to running Flight Instructor courses at Shoreham. She is also a CAA Flight Instructor Examiner. In addition, having qualified as a solicitor in 1982, Dorothy acted for many years as a consultant specialising in aviation and insurance liability issues, and has lectured widely on air law and insurance issues. This highly unusual combination of qualifications led to her appointment as Honorary Solicitor to the Guild of Air Pilots and Navigators (GAPAN). Dorothy is a Fellow of the Royal Aeronautical Society, first Chairman of the GAPAN Instructor Committee, and past Chairman of the Education & Training Committee. She has just completed her term of office as the Master for the year 2014-15 of the Honourable Company of Air Pilots (formerly GAPAN). She is also Chairman of the Professional Flying Instructors Association. In 2003 she was awarded the Jean Lennox Bird Trophy for her contribution to aviation and support of Women in Aviation and the BWPA (British Women Pilots Association). In 2013 Dorothy was awarded the prestigious Master Air Pilots Certificate by GAPAN. A regular contributor to seminars, conferences and aviation publications. Dorothy is the author and editor of a number of flying training books and has published articles in legal and insurance journals.

Daljeet Gill BA(Hons)

Daljeet is the Head of Design & Development for Pooleys Flight Equipment and editor of the Air Pilot's Manuals, Guides to the EASA IR & CPL Flight Test, Pre-flight Briefing and R/T Communications as well as many other publications. Daljeet has been involved with the editing, typesetting and designing of all Pooleys publications and products since she joined us in 2001. Graduating in 1999 with a BA(Hons) in Graphic Design, she deals with marketing, advertising, exhibition design and technical design of our manufactured products in the UK. She maintains our website and produces our Pooleys Catalogue. Daljeet's design skills and imaginative approach have brought a new level of clarity and readability to the projects she has touched.

Sebastian Pooley FRIN FRAeS

Sebastian is Managing Director of Pooleys Flight Equipment and a Director of Air Pilot Publishing. He holds a PPL (A). Sebastian is a Committee Member of the GANG - the General Aviation Navigation Group, part of the Royal Institute of Navigation and a judge for the International Dawn to Dusk Competition. He is a Liveryman of the Honourable Company of Air Pilots, a Fellow of the Royal Institute of Navigation and a Fellow of the Royal Aeronautical Society.

EASA PRIVATE PILOT LICENCE AEROPLANE
FLIGHT PERFORMANCE & PLANNING

Before attempting these practice examination papers, you should have read Air Pilot's Manual, Volume 4 – The Aeroplane Technical and have completed the Progress Tests throughout the manual.

The Flight Performance & Planning examination consists of 12 questions; the time allowed is 45 minutes. Each of the practice examination papers that follow contain 20 questions.

The pass mark is 75%.

Please read each question carefully and ensure you understand it fully before making your choice of answer.

Each question is multiple choice with four possible answers A, B, C and D. You should indicate your chosen answer by placing a cross in the appropriate box on the answer sheet.

Blank answer sheets are to be found at the end of this publication, these may be photocopied.

INTENTIONALLY BLANK

FLIGHT PERFORMANCE AND PLANNING
PAPER 1

1. Aircraft performance tables are often based on:
    a. Cabin altitude
    b. True altitude
    c. True height
    d. Pressure altitude

2. The length of the Take Off Run Available plus the length of any associated clearway is called the:
    a. Accelerate-Stop Distance Available (ASDA)
    b. Maximum Take Off Run Available (MTORA)
    c. Take Off Distance Available (TODA)
    d. Maximum Take Off Distance Available (MTODA)

3. VAT, the target threshold speed, will provide a margin above the stalling speed in the landing configuration of:
    a. 10%
    b. 30%
    c. 50%
    d. 25%

4. From the diagram below: Which profile represents a take off without flap?

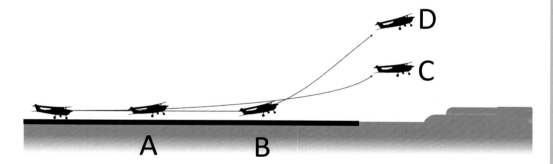

    a. A to C
    b. A to D
    c. B to C
    d. B to D

5. In relation to the position of the Centre of Gravity a light aircraft certified in the "Normal Category" is permitted to undertake:
    a. Normal flying, spinning and angles of bank exceeding 60°
    b. Spinning, but no aerobatic manoeuvres
    c. Normal flying, no spinning or aerobatic manoeuvres and bank angles up to 60°
    d. Manoeuvres exceeding 60° angle of bank and spinning

6. The definition of "Rate of Climb" is:
    a. The amount of height gained per unit of time
    b. The amount of height gained in the shortest horizontal distance
    c. The amount of height gained with the fastest horizontal speed
    d. The amount of height gained in the shortest vertical distance

7. Increasing the all up weight of an aircraft will have what effect on its climb performance?

    a. Climb performance will be degraded

    b. Climb performance will improve

    c. Climb performance will improve a great deal

    d. Climb performance will be unaffected

8. Assume 1 hPa = 30 feet. With an aerodrome elevation of 990 feet and a QFE of 992 hPa, the pressure altitude is:

    a. 1620 ft

    b. 630 ft

    c. 360 ft

    d. 21 ft

9. With an aerodrome elevation of 600 feet and a QFE of 998 hectopascals, the pressure altitude is:

    a. 450 ft

    b. 1050 ft

    c. 15 ft

    d. 548 ft

10. In a piston engine aircraft to fly for maximum range a pilot should select:

    a. The minimum drag speed

    b. A speed just above the stalling speed

    c. A speed just above the minimum drag speed

    d. V_{NO}

11. In a piston engine aircraft to fly for maximum endurance a pilot should select:

    a. The same speed as for maximum range and the lowest safe altitude

    b. A higher speed than for maximum range and the highest altitude possible

    c. A lower speed than for maximum range and the highest altitude possible

    d. A lower airspeed than for maximum range and the lowest safe altitude

12. With which combination of weight and centre of gravity is it safe to fly?

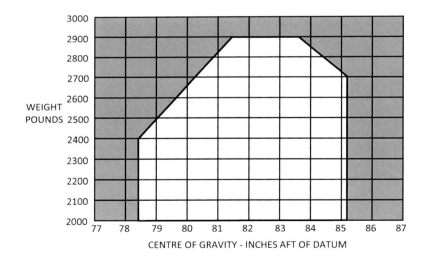

    a. Weight: 2480 C of G position: 78.4

    b. Weight: 2890 C of G position: 81.8

    c. Weight: 2740 C of G position: 80.1

    d. Weight: 2900 C of G position: 85.2

13. An overweight aircraft will:

    a.   Have a lower stalling speed, but a higher take off speed

    b.   Handle and perform poorly and if flown may suffer structural damage

    c.   Have good climb performance and a longer endurance

    d.   Have a longer take off run and a lower take off speed

Use the table above to answer the following three questions.

Maximum Rate of Climb at 2300 pounds Conditions: Full throttle, Flaps up					
Pressure Altitude Feet	Climb Speed KIAS	Rate of Climb - FPM			
		-20°C	0°C	20°C	40°C
S.L.	80	840	780	720	630
2000	79	740	675	615	555
4000	77	675	595	535	475
6000	75	550	485	435	380
8000	73	430	375	320	260
10000	71	330	275	220	165
12000	69	210	145	- - -	- - -

14. For an aircraft weighing 2300 pounds flying at a pressure altitude of 5,000 feet with an OAT of 0°C the maximum rate of climb will be:

    a.   485 fpm

    b.   540 fpm

    c.   635 fpm

    d.   545 fpm

15. For an aircraft weighing 2300 pounds flying at a pressure altitude of 4,000 feet with an OAT of -10°C the maximum rate of climb will be:

    a.   707 fpm

    b.   565 fpm

    c.   655 fpm

    d.   635 fpm

16. For an aircraft weighing 2300 pounds flying at a pressure altitude of 3,000 feet with an OAT of 20°C the maximum rate of climb will be:

    a.   575 fpm

    b.   485 fpm

    c.   595 fpm

    d.   635 fpm

17. In the UK published take off performance is based on a:

    a.   Level and dry short grass surface

    b.   Hard surface with an adverse direction of slope

    c.   Level and dry hard surface

    d.   Level and wet hard surface

18. Complete the following statement: a 2% downslope will ...(i)... the landing distance by approximately ...(ii)...

- **a.** i) increase ii) 20%
- **b.** i) decrease ii) 20%
- **c.** i) increase ii) 10%
- **d.** i) decrease ii) 10%

19. What is the gradient of a 2000 ft runway which has threshold elevations of 415 and 357 feet?

- **a.** 2.9 %
- **b.** 4.05 %
- **c.** 3.2 %
- **d.** 1.9 %

20. Guidelines published in an AIC recommend that when calculating take off distance, the public transport take off factor should be applied to all flights. The factor is:

- **a.** 1.5
- **b.** 1.15
- **c.** 1.33
- **d.** 1.43

END OF FLIGHT PERFORMANCE & PLANNING PAPER 1

INTENTIONALLY BLANK

	A	B	C	D
1.				X
2.			X	
3.		X		
4.				X
5.			X	
6.	X			
7.	X			
8.		X		
9.	X			
10.			X	
11.				X
12.		X		
13.		X		
14.		X		
15				X
16.	X			
17.			X	
18.			X	
19.	X			
20.			X	

CORRECT ANSWERS: PERCENTAGES					
15	16	17	18	19	20
75%	80%	85%	90%	95%	100%

FLIGHT PERFORMANCE AND PLANNING
PAPER 1: EXPLANATIONS

1. **(Answer: D)** Pressure altitude is often used as the datum for measuring aircraft performance. It is the height in the International Standard Atmosphere above the 1013.2 hPa at which the pressure equals that of the aircraft or point in question. Put another way, pressure altitude is the indicated altitude when an altimeter is set to 1013.2 hPa.

    FURTHER READING: APM VOLUME 4, SECTION 4, CHAPTER 31 – TAKE-OFF & LANDING PERFORMANCE

2. **(Answer: C)** The Take-Off Distance Available (TODA) is the length of the take-off run available plus the length of any associated clearway. A clearway is a defined rectangular area of ground or water under the control of the appropriate authority, prepared as a suitable area over which an aeroplane may make an initial portion of its climb to a specified height.

    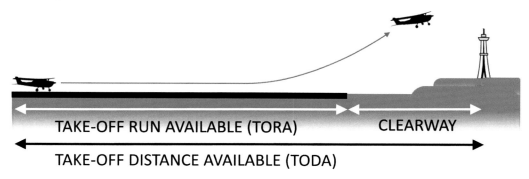

    FURTHER READING: APM VOLUME 4, SECTION 4, CHAPTER 31 – TAKE-OFF & LANDING PERFORMANCE

3. **(Answer: B)** V_{AT}, the target threshold speed, will provide a margin above the stalling speed in the landing configuration of 30%. The target threshold speed is that at which the pilot should aim to cross the threshold and is equal to the stalling speed in the landing configuration (V_{SO}) multiplied by 1.3.

    FURTHER READING: APM VOLUME 4, SECTION 4, CHAPTER 31 – TAKE-OFF & LANDING PERFORMANCE

4. **(Answer: D)** Using small flap settings (up to approximately 20°) during take-off decreases the ground run required. If a large flap setting is used drag will greatly increase and no benefit will be gained; small settings, however, will lower the stalling speed enabling both the lift-off and take-off safety speeds to be reduced. Consequently the aircraft will reach its lift-off speed after a shorter ground roll, meaning that shorter runways can be used or runways with a poor surface can be left behind more quickly!

    Although the ground run is reduced due to the increased lift generated by the flaps, the initial rate and angle of climb will both be reduced due to the increase in drag.

    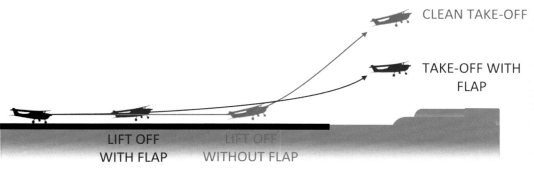

    FURTHER READING: APM VOLUME 4, SECTION 4, CHAPTER 31 – TAKE-OFF & LANDING PERFORMANCE

5.   **(Answer: C)** A light aircraft certified in the "Normal Category" is permitted to undertake normal flying; however spinning and aerobatic manoeuvres are not allowed and bank angles may be restricted to 60°.

EASA Certification Specifications state: The normal category is limited to non-aerobatic operations. Non-aerobatic operations include –
(1)   Any manoeuvre incidental to normal flying;
(2)   Stalls (except whip stalls); and
(3)   Lazy eights, chandelles and steep turns or similar manoeuvres, in which the angle of bank is not more than 60°.

The utility category is limited to any of the operations covered in the normal category; plus -
(1)   Spins (if approved for the particular type of aeroplane); and
(2)   Lazy eights, chandelles, and steep turns, or similar manoeuvres in which the angle of bank is more than 60° but not more than 90°.

The aerobatic category is without restrictions, other than those shown to be necessary as a result of required flight tests EASA-CS 23.3.

See also the UK General Aviation Safety Sense Leaflet number 9.

FURTHER READING: APM VOLUME 4, SECTION 4, CHAPTER 33 – MASS & BALANCE

6.   **(Answer: A)** Rate of Climb is defined as the amount of height gained per unit of time. time.

FURTHER READING: APM VOLUME 4, SECTION 1, CHAPTER 11 – CLIMBING

7.   **(Answer: A)** Increasing the all up weight of an aircraft will degrade climb performance. The more excess power that is available the greater the rate of climb that can be achieved. Increasing weight will require more lift to balance it, leading to the production of more drag and the necessity to use more power to overcome the drag. As a consequence excess power available will be less and climb performance will degrade.

Factors reducing climb performance:
Weight increased
Altitude increases (lower air density)
Temperature increased (lower air density)

FURTHER READING: APM VOLUME 4, SECTION 1, CHAPTER 11 – CLIMBING

8. **(Answer: B)** 630 feet. Pressure altitude is often used as the datum for measuring aircraft performance. It is the height in the International Standard Atmosphere above 1013.2 hPa at which the pressure equals that of the aircraft or point in question. Put another way, pressure altitude is the indicated altitude when an altimeter is set to 1013.2 hPa.

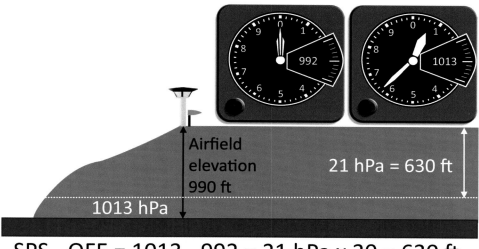

$$\text{SPS - QFE} = 1013 - 992 = 21 \text{ hPa} \times 30 = 630 \text{ ft}$$

FURTHER READING: APM VOLUME 4, SECTION 3, CHAPTER 25 – PRESSURE INSTRUMENTS

9. **(Answer: A)** 450 feet. Pressure altitude is often used as the datum for measuring aircraft performance. It is the height in the International Standard Atmosphere above the 1013.2 hPa at which the pressure equals that of the aircraft or point in question. Put another way, pressure altitude is the indicated altitude when an altimeter is set to 1013.2 hPa.

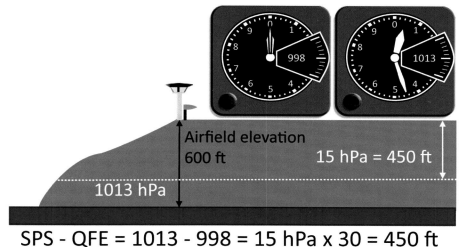

$$\text{SPS - QFE} = 1013 - 998 = 15 \text{ hPa} \times 30 = 450 \text{ ft}$$

FURTHER READING: APM VOLUME 4, SECTION 3, CHAPTER 25 – PRESSURE INSTRUMENTS

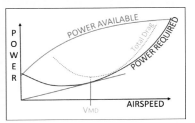

10. ANSWER C

10. **(Answer: C)** In a piston engine aircraft to fly for maximum range a pilot should select a speed just above the minimum drag speed. To achieve maximum range the aircraft must consume the lowest amount of fuel possible for each nautical mile travelled, this will be where the power to airspeed ratio is the least. To find this point graphically a tangent is drawn from the origin to the power required curve, this is where the power to speed ratio is the smallest and corresponds to the minimum drag speed.

In practical terms a piston engine is at its most efficient at around 65% power, and taking engine efficiency into account, will give airspeed slightly higher than minimum drag speed. The maximum range speed will be 5 to 10% faster than the minimum drag speed.

FURTHER READING: APM VOLUME 4, SECTION 4, CHAPTER 32 – ENROUTE PERFORMANCE

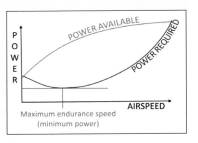

11. ANSWER D

11. **(Answer: D)** In a piston engine aircraft, to fly for maximum endurance a pilot should select a lower airspeed than for maximum range and the lowest safe altitude. Maximum endurance means spending the longest possible time airborne, which equates to flying at a speed that will require the minimum amount of power.

The second part of the question asks you to select the most desirable altitude. Flying at the lowest safe level means flying at a lower true airspeed which means that the power required to overcome drag is reduced.

Power required = drag x true airspeed

When maintaining a constant indicated airspeed (IAS), true airspeed (TAS) will increase with increase in altitude. The easiest way to picture this is to imagine an aircraft in a climb; to maintain a constant IAS the value of dynamic pressure must remain the same. Dynamic pressure is ½ density x velocity^2, therefore as the air density decreases with increase in altitude to maintain a constant dynamic pressure the velocity must increase.

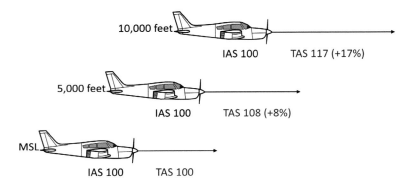

FURTHER READING: APM VOLUME 4, SECTION 4, CHAPTER 32 – ENROUTE PERFORMANCE

12. **(Answer: B)** In order to be loaded safely, plot the values for mass and centre of gravity on the graph to find whether they fall within the CG envelope. The white area of the graph represents the weight and balance envelope, the only values given that fall within its parameters are: weight 2890 and C of G position 81.8

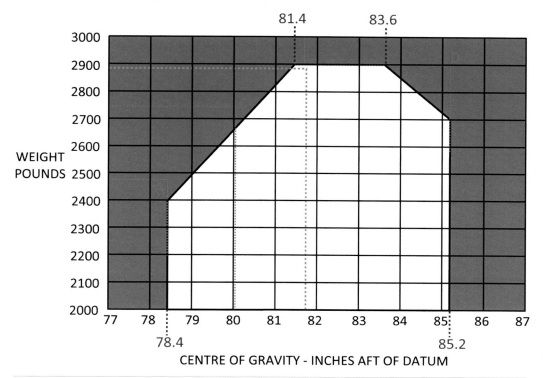

CENTRE OF GRAVITY - INCHES AFT OF DATUM

FURTHER READING: APM VOLUME 4, SECTION 4, CHAPTER 31 —TAKE-OFF & LANDING PERFORMANCE

13. **(Answer: B)** An overweight aircraft will handle and perform poorly, and if flown may suffer structural damage. Other effects of increased weight are:

Higher take off speed
Longer take off run
Higher stalling speed
Reduced climb performance (both rate and angle of climb)
Increased fuel consumption and so less endurance
Shorter range
Higher landing speed and longer landing distance
Reduced manoeuvrability

FURTHER READING: APM VOLUME 4, SECTION 4, CHAPTER 31 —TAKE-OFF & LANDING PERFORMANCE

14. **(Answer: B)** In the performance table pressure altitudes are given at 2,000 ft intervals. Thus to find the maximum rate of climb at 5,000 feet with an OAT of 0°C we must interpolate between the figures given.

Maximum Rate of Climb at 2300 pounds Conditions: Full throttle, Flaps up					
Pressure Altitude Feet	Climb Speed KIAS	Rate of Climb - FPM			
		-20°C	0°C	20°C	40°C
S.L.	80	840	780	720	630
2000	79	740	675	615	555
4000	77	675	**595**	535	475
6000	75	550	**485**	435	380
8000	73	430	375	320	260
10000	71	330	275	220	165
12000	69	210	145	- - -	- - -

At 4,000 feet in the 0°C column we find the maximum rate of climb is 595 fpm; at 6000 feet it is 485 fpm. To find the value at 5,000 feet add these two values together and, as 5,000 feet is exactly half way in between the given values, divide by 2.

$$595 + 485 = 1080 \div 2 = 540 \text{ fpm}$$

FURTHER READING: APM VOLUME 4, SECTION 1, CHAPTER 11 – CLIMBING

15. **(Answer: D)** In the performance table temperatures are given at 20 degree intervals. Thus to find the maximum rate of climb at 4,000 feet with an OAT of -10°C we must interpolate between the figures given.

Maximum Rate of Climb at 2300 pounds Conditions: Full throttle, Flaps up					
Pressure Altitude Feet	Climb Speed KIAS	Rate of Climb - FPM			
		-20°C	0°C	20°C	40°C
S.L.	80	840	780	720	630
2000	79	740	675	615	555
4000	77	**675**	**595**	535	475
6000	75	550	485	435	380
8000	73	430	375	320	260
10000	71	330	275	220	165
12000	69	210	145	- - -	- - -

At 4,000 feet in the 0°C column we find the maximum rate of climb is 595 fpm; in the -20°C column it is 675 fpm. To find the value for -10°C add these two values together and, as -10°C is exactly half way in between the given values, divide by 2.

$$595 + 675 = 1270 \div 2 = 635 \text{ fpm}$$

FURTHER READING: APM VOLUME 4, SECTION 1, CHAPTER 11 – CLIMBING

16. **(Answer: A)** In the performance table pressure altitudes are given at 2,000 ft intervals. Thus to find the maximum rate of climb at 3,000 feet with an OAT of 20°C we must interpolate between the figures given.

Maximum Rate of Climb at 2300 pounds					
Conditions: Full throttle, Flaps up					
Pressure Altitude Feet	Climb Speed KIAS	Rate of Climb - FPM			
		-20°C	0°C	20°C	40°C
S.L.	80	840	780	720	630
2000	79	740	675	**615**	555
4000	77	675	595	**535**	475
6000	75	550	485	435	380
8000	73	430	375	320	260
10000	71	330	275	220	165
12000	69	210	145	- - -	- - -

At 4,000 feet in the 20°C column we find the maximum rate of climb is 535 fpm; at 2000 feet it is 615 fpm. To find the value at 3,000 feet add these two values together and, as 3,000 feet is exactly half way in between the given values, divide by 2.

615 + 535 =1150 ÷ 2 = 575 fpm

FURTHER READING: APM VOLUME 4, SECTION 1, CHAPTER 11 – CLIMBING

17. **(Answer: C)** Take off performance data in the UK is based on a hard surface that is level and dry. The friction created by other surfaces, for example grass, will slow acceleration on the ground and increase the take off distance.

Short dry grass increases the take off distance by 20%, short wet grass by 25%
Long dry grass increases the take off distance by 25%, long wet grass by 30%
Soft ground or snow will increase the take off distance by at least 25%, probably more.

FURTHER READING: APM VOLUME 4, SECTION 4, CHAPTER 31 – TAKE-OFF & LANDING PERFORMANCE

18. **(Answer: C)** The landing distance will increase by 10% for each 2% of downhill slope (a factor of x 1.10). AIC 127/2006 (Pink 110)

FURTHER READING: APM VOLUME 4, SECTION 4, CHAPTER 31 – TAKE-OFF & LANDING PERFORMANCE

19. **(Answer: A)** To calculate the runway gradient:

$$\frac{\text{Higher threshold} - \text{Lower threshold}}{\text{Runway length}} \times \frac{100}{1}$$

$$\frac{415 - 357}{2000} \times \frac{100}{1} = 2.9\%$$

FURTHER READING: APM VOLUME 4, SECTION 4, CHAPTER 31 – TAKE-OFF & LANDING PERFORMANCE

20. **(Answer: C)** It is recommended that, at least, the public transport factors should be applied for all flights. Unless otherwise specified in the aeroplanes manual, handbook or supplement, as factor of 1.33 for take-off is recommended, and should be applied after other variables have been accounted for. AIC 127/2006 (Pink 110).

FURTHER READING: APM VOLUME 4, SECTION 4, CHAPTER 31 – TAKE-OFF & LANDING PERFORMANCE

END OF EXPLANATIONS PAPER 1

1. The airspeed to fly to achieve maximum range is:

    a. The minimum power speed

    b. The speed where power available equals power required

    c. The never exceed speed

    d. The speed where the power: airspeed ratio is least

2. In comparison to a flapless take off, using a small flap setting for take off will:

    a. Increase the stalling, lift off and take off safety speeds

    b. Reduce the stalling and lift off speeds, but will increase the take off safety speed

    c. Reduce the stalling, lift off and take off safety speeds

    d. Reduce the stalling speed, but increase the lift off and take off safety speeds

3. With which combination of weight and centre of gravity is it safe to fly?

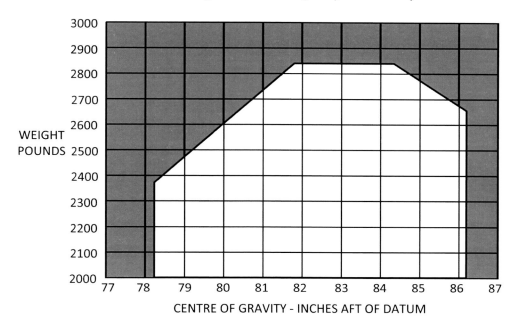

    a. Weight: 2480 C of G position: 78.4

    b. Weight: 2830 C of G position: 86.2

    c. Weight: 2810 C of G position: 84.4

    d. Weight: 2750 C of G position: 80.5

4. An increase in aircraft weight of 10% will ...(i)... the landing distance by ...(ii)...

    a. i) reduce   ii) a factor of 1.1, or 10%

    b. i) increase   ii) a factor of 1.43, or 43%

    c. i) reduce   ii) a factor of 1.43, or 43%

    d. i) increase   ii) a factor of 1.1, or 10%

5. Using a runway with a down slope will require:

    a. A longer landing distance, and a longer take off distance

    b. A longer landing distance, but a shorter take off distance

    c. A shorter landing distance, and a shorter take off distance

    d. A shorter landing distance, but a longer take off distance

6. Compared to an aerodrome at sea level, when operating from an aerodrome having a high pressure altitude will lead to:

    a. A longer landing distance, and a longer take off distance

    b. A longer landing distance, but a shorter take off distance

    c. A shorter landing distance, and a shorter take off distance

    d. A shorter landing distance, but a longer take off distance

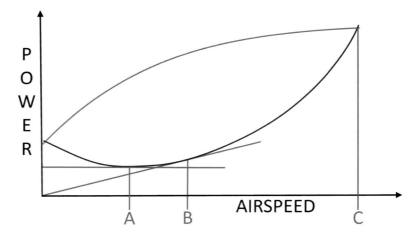

7. Assuming that fuel consumption is directly related to the power delivered by the engine, which point represents the airspeed at which to fly for maximum endurance?

    a. C or A depending on the aircraft's weight

    b. C

    c. B

    d. A

8. If the stalling speed of a particular aircraft in the landing configuration (V_{so}) is 50 KTS, therefore the minimum approach speed is approximately:

    a. 72 KTS

    b. 65 KTS

    c. 68 KTS

    d. 60 KTS

Refer to the Take Off Performance Graph opposite to answer the following three questions:

9. *Given:*

OAT: +15°C
Pressure Altitude: Sea Level
Aircraft Weight: 3100 lbs
Surface Wind: 20 knots Headwind

What is the approximate take off distance required to reach a screen height of 50 ft?

    a. 1,000 feet

    b. 1,500 feet

    c. 900 feet

    d. 1,100 feet

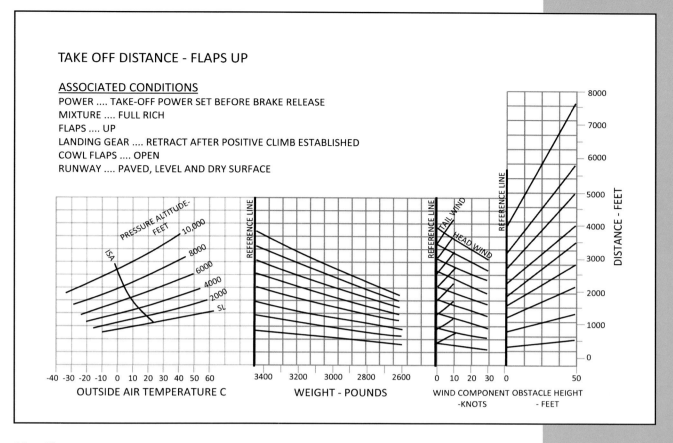

TAKE OFF DISTANCE - FLAPS UP

<u>ASSOCIATED CONDITIONS</u>
POWER .... TAKE-OFF POWER SET BEFORE BRAKE RELEASE
MIXTURE .... FULL RICH
FLAPS .... UP
LANDING GEAR .... RETRACT AFTER POSITIVE CLIMB ESTABLISHED
COWL FLAPS .... OPEN
RUNWAY .... PAVED, LEVEL AND DRY SURFACE

10. *Given:*

OAT:	+20°C
Pressure Altitude:	1,000 feet
Aircraft Weight:	3300 lbs
Surface Wind:	Calm

What is the approximate take off distance required to reach a screen height of 50 ft?

a. 1,950 feet
b. 2,200 feet
c. 1,450 feet
d. 1,700 feet

11. *Given:*

OAT:	-5°C
Pressure Altitude:	Sea Level
Aircraft Weight:	3400 lbs
Surface Wind:	5 knots Tailwind

What is the approximate take off distance required to reach a screen height of 50 ft?

a. 1,350 feet
b. 1,850 feet
c. 2,100 feet
d. 1,050 feet

12. When landing with a tailwind, the ground speed will be:

a. Less than the TAS
b. The same as the TAS
c. Greater than the TAS
d. Slightly less than the TAS

13. With regard to the diagram below showing the variation of power available and power required by a piston engine aircraft over a range of speeds. Assuming that fuel consumption is directly related to the power generated by the engine, which point represents the speed to fly to obtain maximum range?

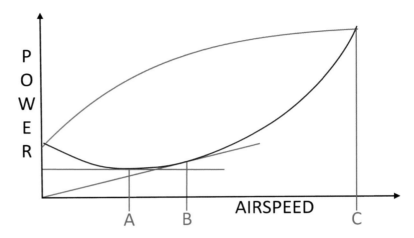

a.   C or A depending on the aircraft's weight

b.   C

c.   B

d.   A

14. An aircraft having a lift:drag ratio of 6:1 will have a maximum gliding distance from 5,000 feet in still air of approximately:

a.   6 nm

b.   5 nm

c.   4 nm

d.   3 nm

15. When compared to a lightly loaded aircraft, to achieve the maximum glide range in a heavy aircraft:

a.   A steeper glide angle must be used

b.   A shallower glide angle must be used

c.   A slower speed must be used

d.   A faster speed must be used

16. Increasing an aircraft's weight by 10% will have what effect on its take off distance?

a.   Take off distance will increase by 20%

b.   Take off distance will increase by 33%

c.   Take off distance will reduce by 20%

d.   Take off distance will reduce by 43%

17. Which picture represents the Zero Fuel Mass?

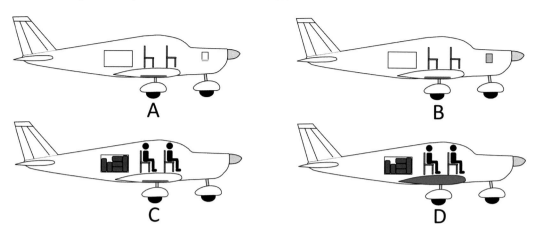

A   B

C   D

    a.   A
    b.   B
    c.   C
    d.   D

18. Using a higher airspeed than that recommended in the Flight Manual during an approach to landing will have what effect?

    a.   It will have no effect other than you will arrive earlier
    b.   It will increase the landing distance
    c.   It will reduce the landing distance, but increase the braking distance required
    d.   It will reduce the landing distance required

19. Ice on an aircraft's wings will:

    a.   Increase weight, but decrease drag
    b.   Increase weight and drag, and seriously reduce the lift generated
    c.   No change in weight
    d.   Reduce the lift generated, but have no effect on drag

20. With all tanks full an aircraft holds 230 litres of fuel. If the specific gravity (SG) of the fuel is 0.72, what is the approximate weight of the fuel in pounds?

    a.   166 lbs
    b.   364 lbs
    c.   703 lbs
    d.   75 lbs

END OF FLIGHT PERFORMANCE AND PLANNING PAPER 2

	A	B	C	D
1.				X
2.			X	
3.			X	
4.				X
5.		X		
6.	X			
7.				X
8.		X		
9.				X
10.	X			
11.		X		
12.			X	
13.			X	
14.		X		
15				X
16.	X			
17.			X	
18.		X		
19.		X		
20.		X		

CORRECT ANSWERS: PERCENTAGES					
15	16	17	18	19	20
75%	80%	85%	90%	95%	100%

1. **(Answer: D)** In a piston engine aircraft to fly for maximum range a pilot should select a speed just above the minimum drag speed. To achieve maximum range the aircraft must consume the lowest amount of fuel possible for each nautical mile travelled, this will be where the power: airspeed ratio is the least. To find this point graphically a tangent is drawn from the origin to the power available curve, this is where the power: speed ratio is the smallest and corresponds to the minimum drag speed.

   In practical terms a piston engine is at its most efficient at around 65% power, and taking engine efficiency into account, will give airspeed slightly higher than minimum drag speed. The maximum range speed will be 5 to 10% faster than the minimum drag speed.

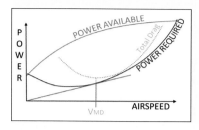

1. ANSWER D

FURTHER READING: APM VOLUME 4, SECTION 4, CHAPTER 32 – ENROUTE PERFORMANCE

2. **(Answer: C)** Using small flap settings (up to approximately 20°) during take-off will generate extra lift with a relatively small increase in drag. As a consequence an aircraft will be able to take off at a slower speed and with a shorter ground run.

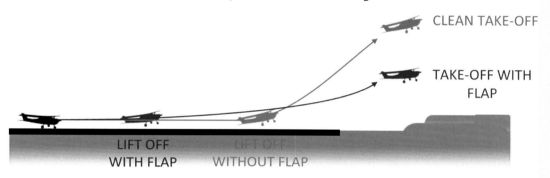

Extending flap changes the shape of the aerofoil to one with a higher C_LMAX, meaning that the same weight can be supported at a lower speed.

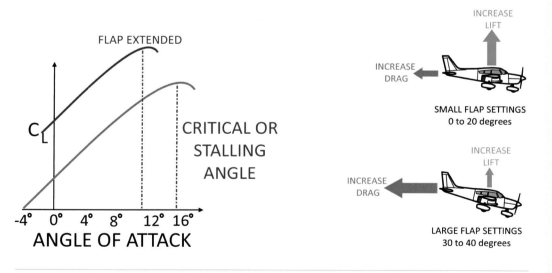

FURTHER READING: APM VOLUME 4, SECTION 4, CHAPTER 31 – TAKE-OFF & LANDING PERFORMANCE

3. **(Answer: C)** In order to be loaded safely, plot the values for mass and centre of gravity on the graph to find whether they fall within the CG envelope. The white area of the graph represents the weight and balance envelope: the only values given that fall within its parameters are: weight 2810 and C of G position 84.4

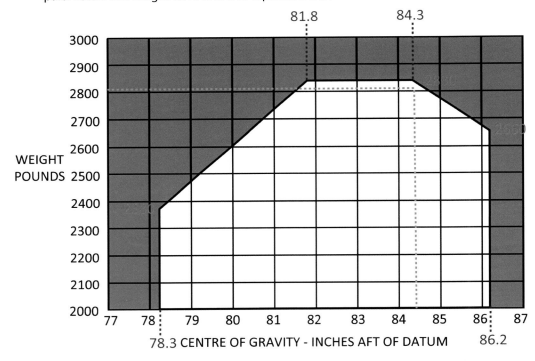

4. **(Answer: D)** Increased weight will increase the landing distance, because the stalling speed will increase and consequently the minimum approach speed (1.3 x V_{so}) will increase. A higher landing speed means that the aircraft will require more distance to stop. Additionally the higher kinetic energy must be absorbed by the brakes which will also increase the landing run.

From AIC 127/2006 (Pink 110): Guide line factor: landing distance will be increased by 10% for each 10% increase in aeroplane weight (a factor of x 1.10).

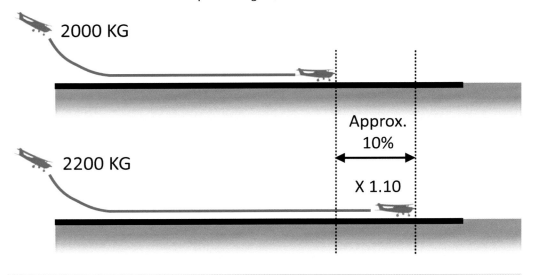

5.   **(Answer: B)** A runway with a downhill slope will increase the landing distance and will decrease the take off distance as the aircraft will accelerate faster. A 2% down slope will increase the landing distance by 10%, a factor of 1.1. AIC 127/2006 (Pink 110)

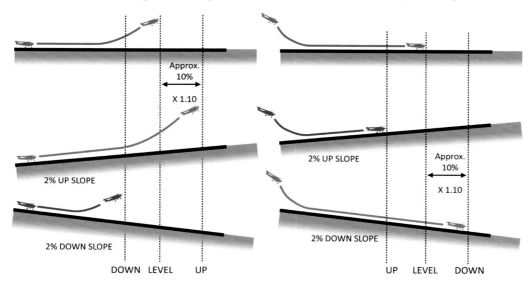

FURTHER READING: APM VOLUME 4, SECTION 4, CHAPTER 31 – TAKE-OFF & LANDING PERFORMANCE

6.   **(Answer: A)** Aircraft performance deteriorates with an increase in altitude and the pressure altitude at the aerodrome should be used for calculations. This equates to the height shown on the altimeter on the ground at the aerodrome with the sub-scale set at 1013 hPa. Take-off distance will be increased by 10% for each 1000 ft increase in aerodrome altitude (a factor of x 1.10).

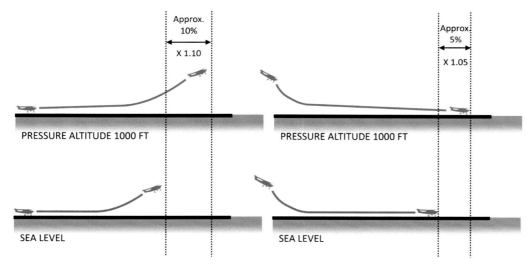

Landing distance will be increased by 5% for each 1000 ft increase in aerodrome pressure altitude (a factor of x 1.05).

FURTHER READING: APM VOLUME 4, SECTION 4, CHAPTER 31 – TAKE-OFF & LANDING PERFORMANCE

7.   **(Answer: D)** Maximum endurance means spending the longest possible time airborne, it equates to flying at a speed that will require the minimum amount of power.

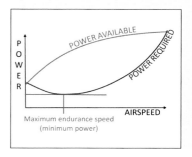

FURTHER READING: APM VOLUME 4, SECTION 4, CHAPTER 32 – ENROUTE PERFORMANCE

7. ANSWER D

8.   **(Answer: B)** 65 knots. V_{REF}, the reference landing approach speed, will provide a margin above the stalling speed in the landing configuration of 30%. This applies to normal, utility and aerobatic category aircraft of less than 2,722 kg (6,000 lbs) or less and is equal to the stalling speed in the landing configuration (V_{SO}) multiplied by 1.3. EASA-CS 23.73.

FURTHER READING: APM VOLUME 4, SECTION 4, CHAPTER 31 – TAKE-OFF & LANDING PERFORMANCE

---

9.   **(Answer: D)** 1,100 feet

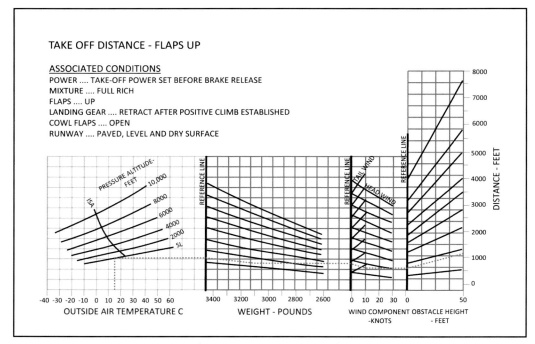

OAT: +15 PA: Sea Level A/C Weight: 3100 lbs Wind: H/W 20 Knots OBSTACLE: 50 FT

1.   Enter the graph from the bottom at +15°C and draw a line vertically upwards to the actual pressure altitude, in this case sea level.
2.   Draw a horizontal line to the first reference line
3.   Follow the direction of the nearest "weight" lines until the take-off weight, 3100 lbs, is reached.
4.   From this point draw a horizontal line to the second reference line.
5.   Parallel the nearest lines representing headwind remembering, unless otherwise stated, to use only **50% of the reported headwind**. In this case use 10 knots.
6.   Again, draw a horizontal line this time to the third reference line.
7.   Finally, follow the nearest lines to obtain the 50 ft screen height figure.

NOTE: TO THIS FIGURE WE SHOULD THEN ADD THE TAKE OFF SAFETY FACTOR OF 1.33, TOGETHER WITH ANY ADDITIONAL FACTORS FOR RUNWAY SURFACE, SLOPE ETC.. THAT MAY BE NECESSARY.

FURTHER READING: APM VOLUME 4, SECTION 4, CHAPTER 31 – TAKE-OFF & LANDING PERFORMANCE

---

10. (Answer: A) 1,950 feet.

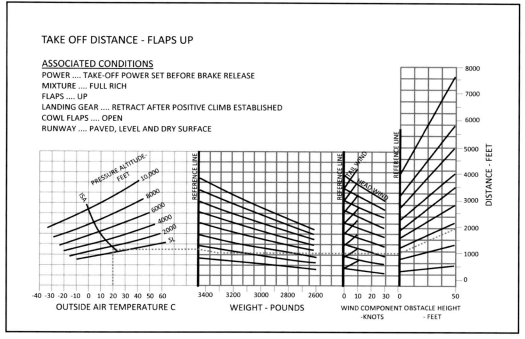

OAT: +20 PA: 1000 A/c Weight: 3300 Wind: Calm Obstacle: 50 FT

1. Enter the graph from the bottom at +20°C and draw a line vertically upwards to the actual pressure altitude, in this case 1,000 feet.
2. Draw a horizontal line to the first reference line
3. Follow the direction of the nearest "weight" lines until the take-off weight, 3300 lbs, is reached.
4. From this point draw a horizontal line to the second reference point.
5. As the wind is calm continue this horizontal line all the way to the third reference line.
6. Finally, parallel the nearest lines to obtain the 50 ft screen height figure.

NOTE: TO THIS FIGURE WE SHOULD THEN ADD THE TAKE OFF SAFETY FACTOR OF 1.33, TOGETHER WITH ANY ADDITIONAL FACTORS FOR RUNWAY SURFACE, SLOPE ETC.. THAT MAY BE NECESSARY.

FURTHER READING: APM VOLUME 4, SECTION 4, CHAPTER 31 – TAKE-OFF & LANDING PERFORMANCE

11. (Answer: B) 1,850 feet

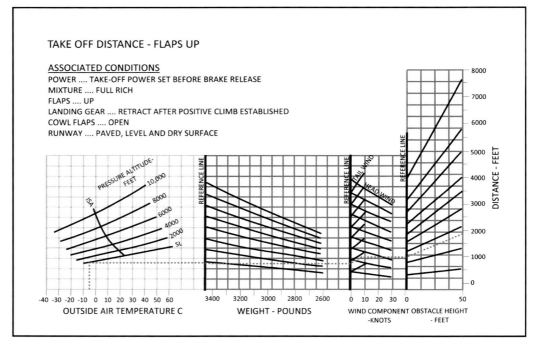

TAKE OFF DISTANCE - FLAPS UP

ASSOCIATED CONDITIONS
POWER .... TAKE-OFF POWER SET BEFORE BRAKE RELEASE
MIXTURE .... FULL RICH
FLAPS .... UP
LANDING GEAR .... RETRACT AFTER POSITIVE CLIMB ESTABLISHED
COWL FLAPS .... OPEN
RUNWAY .... PAVED, LEVEL AND DRY SURFACE

OAT: -5 PA: Sea Level A/c Weight: 3400 lbs Wind: 5 knot tailwind Obstacle: 50 FT

1. Enter the graph from the bottom at -5°C and draw a line vertically upwards to the actual pressure altitude, in this case sea level.

2. Draw a horizontal line to the first reference line

3. Follow the direction of the nearest "weight" lines until the take-off weight, 3400 lbs, is reached.

4. From this point draw a horizontal line to the second reference point.

5. Parallel the nearest lines representing tailwind remembering, unless otherwise stated, to use **150% of the reported tailwind**. In this case use 7.5 knots.

6. Again, draw a horizontal line this time to the third reference line.

7. Finally, follow the nearest lines to obtain the 50 ft screen height figure.

NOTE: TO THIS FIGURE WE SHOULD THEN ADD THE TAKE OFF SAFETY FACTOR OF 1.33, TOGETHER WITH ANY ADDITIONAL FACTORS FOR RUNWAY SURFACE, SLOPE ETC.. THAT MAY BE NECESSARY.

FURTHER READING: APM VOLUME 4, SECTION 4, CHAPTER 31 – TAKE-OFF & LANDING PERFORMANCE

---

12. (Answer: C) A tailwind means that the ground speed will be greater than the TAS. The consequences of this are a higher touchdown speed and a longer landing run.

FFURTHER READING: APM VOLUME 4, SECTION 4, CHAPTER 31 – TAKE-OFF & LANDING PERFORMANCE

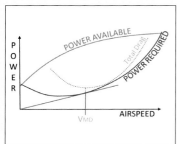

13. ANSWER C

13. (Answer: C) In a piston engine aircraft to fly for maximum range a pilot should select a speed just above the minimum drag speed. To achieve maximum range the aircraft must consume the lowest amount of fuel possible for each nautical mile travelled, this will be where the power: airspeed ratio is the least. To find this point graphically a tangent is drawn from the origin to the power required curve, this is where the power: speed ratio is the smallest and corresponds to the minimum drag speed.

In practical terms a piston engine is at its most efficient at around 65% power, and taking engine efficiency into account, will give airspeed slightly higher than minimum drag speed. The maximum range speed will be 5 to 10% faster than the minimum drag speed.

FURTHER READING: APM VOLUME 4, SECTION 4, CHAPTER 32 – ENROUTE PERFORMANCE

14. **(Answer: B)** A lift: drag ratio of 6:1 will glide 6 times as far as it descends. For each 1,000 feet of height lost the aircraft will travel 6,000 feet horizontally.

Therefore from 5,000 feet:
6 x 5,000 = 30,000 feet
30,000 ÷ 6,000 = 5 nm

I nm is equal to 6080 feet (near enough 6,000 feet), so the aircraft will glide approximately 5 nm.

FURTHER READING: APM VOLUME 4, SECTION 1, CHAPTER 12 – DESCENDING

15. **(Answer: D)** Aircraft weight does not affect the gliding range, the best lift: drag ratio is achieved at a particular angle of attack. The factor that does alter is the glide speed; a heavier aircraft will need to have a higher airspeed at any given angle of attack than a lighter aircraft. This is because more lift is required to balance the greater weight. For a heavier aircraft both lift and drag will need to increase but the proportions will remain the same.

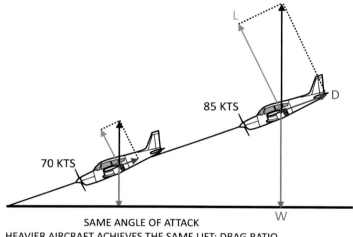

SAME ANGLE OF ATTACK
HEAVIER AIRCRAFT ACHIEVES THE SAME LIFT: DRAG RATIO
AT A HIGHER SPEED

FURTHER READING: APM VOLUME 4, SECTION 1, CHAPTER 12 – DESCENDING

16. **(Answer: A)** Increased weight on departure will mean slower acceleration and increased friction from the extra weight on wheels – leading to more distance being used up.

From AIC 127/2006 Pink 110: Guide line factor: take off distance will be increased by 20% for each 10% increase in aeroplane weight (a factor of x 1.20).

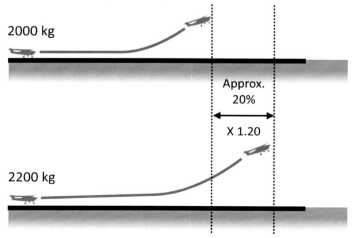

FURTHER READING: APM VOLUME 4, SECTION 4, CHAPTER 31 – TAKE-OFF & LANDING PERFORMANCE

17. **(Answer: C)**

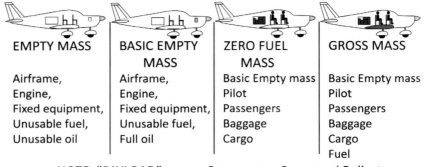

EMPTY MASS	BASIC EMPTY MASS	ZERO FUEL MASS	GROSS MASS
Airframe, Engine, Fixed equipment, Unusable fuel, Unusable oil	Airframe, Engine, Fixed equipment, Unusable fuel, Full oil	Basic Empty mass Pilot Passengers Baggage Cargo	Basic Empty mass Pilot Passengers Baggage Cargo Fuel

NOTE: "PAYLOAD" means Passengers, Cargo and Ballast

FURTHER READING: APM VOLUME 4, SECTION 4, CHAPTER 33 – MASS & BALANCE

18. **(Answer: B)** Landing performance charts are based on flying the specified approach speed. If a faster speed is adopted the landing distance will exceed that predicted by the chart.

FURTHER READING: APM VOLUME 4, SECTION 4, CHAPTER 31 – TAKE-OFF & LANDING PERFORMANCE

19. **(Answer: B)** Ice accretion on wings adds a great deal of weight and significantly increases drag. Additionally it can drastically reduce the lift generated by a wing; this is especially true when ice forms on the upper surface.

FURTHER READING: APM VOLUME 4, SECTION 1, CHAPTER 10 – STRAIGHT & LEVEL

20. **(Answer: B)** There are two ways to tackle these problems either mathematically or using the CRP Flight Computer.

Mathematically: a specific gravity of 0.72 means that Avgas weighs only 0.72 times as much as an equal volume of water. One litre of water weighs 1 kg, so one litre of Avgas weighs 0.72 kg. **230 litres x 0.72 = 165.6 kg**

However we are asked for an answer in pounds: **165.6 x 2.2 = 364.3 lbs**

CRP-1: Set the number of litres (230 lt) under the litres index on the fixed outer scale. Notice on the fixed outer scale are two scales for specific gravity (Sp. G) one in kg and one in lbs. Below 72 on the Imperial Sp. G scale read off 364 lb on the INNER rotating scale.

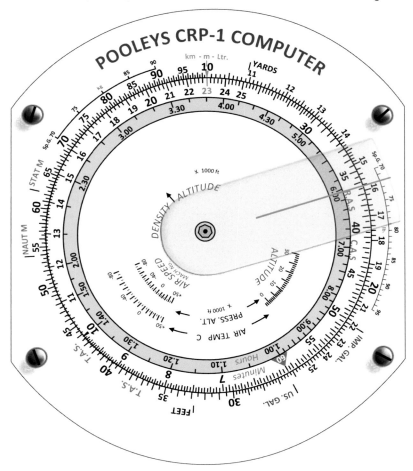

FURTHER READING: APM VOLUME 4, SECTION 4, CHAPTER 33 – MASS & BALANCE

END OF EXPLANATIONS PAPER 2

INTENTIONALLY BLANK

FLIGHT PERFORMANCE AND PLANNING
PAPER 3

1. Using a runway with an up slope will require:

    a. A longer landing distance, and a longer take off distance

    b. A longer landing distance, but a shorter take off distance

    c. A shorter landing distance, and a shorter take off distance

    d. A shorter landing distance, but a longer take off distance

2. You are completing the following loading form:

Max Take off Mass Authorised 2400 lbs
Max Landing Mass Authorised 2300 lbs
CG limits: 18 to 22 inches aft of datum

Item	Mass (lb)	Arm	Moment (lb In)
Basic Mass	1600	+27	+43,200
Pilot & Front Passenger	320	−6	−1,920
Oil (SG 0.8)	30	−17	−510
Rear Passengers	140	+24	+3,360
Baggage	10	+42	+420
Fuel (SG 0.72)		+20	
TOTAL			

What is the maximum amount of fuel in litres that may be safely loaded?

    a. 136 l

    b. 189 l

    c. 416 l

    d. 317 l

3. If the aircraft is fuelled with 250 lbs of fuel, of which 200 lbs will be burned during the flight, what is the CG position on departure and on landing?

Max Take off Mass Authorised 2400 lbs
Max Landing Mass Authorised 2300 lbs
CG limits: 18 to 22 inches aft of datum

Item	Mass (lb)	Arm	Moment (lb In)
Basic Mass	1600	+27	+43,200
Pilot & Front Passenger	320	−6	−1,920
Oil (SG 0.8)	30	−17	−510
Rear Passengers	140	+24	+3,360
Baggage	10	+42	+420
Fuel (SG 0.72)		+20	
TOTAL			

    a. CG position on departure: 21.08 CG position on landing: 21.18

    b. CG position on departure: 20.4 CG position on landing: 28.91

    c. CG position on departure: 21.18 CG position on landing: 21.68

    d. CG position on departure: 22.01 CG position on landing: 22. 10

4. Given:

Aircraft planned take-off weight: 2300 lb
CG on departure: 85.75 inches aft of datum
Fuel burn: 300 lb (position 82 inches aft of datum)

On landing what is the calculated CG position?

a. 86.31 inches aft of datum
b. 110.9 inches aft of datum
c. 75.05 inches aft of datum
d. 66.39 inches aft of datum

5. Given:

Aircraft planned take-off weight: 2200 lb
CG on departure: 84.75 inches aft of datum
Fuel burn: 200 lb (position 81 inches aft of datum)

On landing what is the calculated CG position?
a. 70.94 inches aft of datum
b. 101.3 inches aft of datum
c. 88.225 inches aft of datum
d. 85.125 inches aft of datum

6. Given:

Aircraft planned take-off weight: 2300 lb
CG on departure: 90.75 inches aft of datum
Fuel burn: 170 lb (position 87 inches aft of datum)

On landing what is the calculated CG position?

a. 78.52 inches aft of datum
b. 91.05 inches aft of datum
c. 89.88 inches aft of datum
d. 90.49 inches aft of datum

7. Before refuelling an aircraft weighs 1800 lbs, the total moment was 151,200 lb in. 310 lb of fuel are then loaded having an arm 90 inches aft of the datum. The total moment is...(i)... and the aircraft's CG will now be ...(ii)...:

a. i) 123,300 lb in   ii) 82.75 inches aft of the datum
b. i) 155,200 lb in   ii) 73.55 inches aft of the datum
c. i) 133,400 lb in   ii) 83.01 inches aft of the datum
d. i) 179,100 lb in   ii) 84.88 inches aft of the datum

8. Before refuelling an aircraft weighs 1900 lbs, the total moment was 162,200 lb in. 400 lb of fuel are then loaded having an arm 12 ft aft of the datum. The aircraft's CG will now be:

a. 72.60 inches aft of the datum
b. 95.56 inches aft of the datum
c. 69.73 inches aft of the datum
d. 111.33 inches aft of the datum

9. Selecting full flap on approach allows a pilot to adopt a ... (i)... approach path and/or a ...(ii)...approach speed.

   a.   i) more shallow   ii) faster

   b.   i) steeper   ii) slower

   c.   i) steeper   ii) faster

   d.   i) more shallow   ii) slower

10. An overloaded aircraft:

   a.   May have a longer take-off run but will have good climb performance

   b.   Will have a lower stalling speed and be more manoeuvrable

   c.   Will handle and perform badly and, if flown, may suffer structural damage

   d.   May have a lower take-off speed and a shorter range

11. By how much should you expect the landing distance to increase when landing on very short, wet grass with firm soil?

   a.   60%

   b.   50%

   c.   40%

   d.   30%

12. An aircraft is loaded as follows:

Departure mass: 1010 kg
Total moment: 930 kg.m

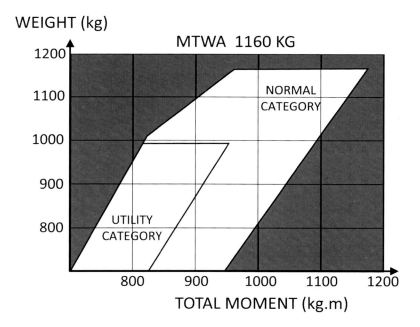

With reference to the centre of gravity envelope chart below which of the following statements is correct?

   a.   The aircraft centre of gravity lies within the utility category and angles of bank exceeding 60° are permitted

   b.   The aircraft centre of gravity lies within the normal category and angles of bank exceeding 60° are permitted

   c.   The aircraft centre of gravity lies within the utility category and angles of bank exceeding 60° are not permitted

   d.   The aircraft centre of gravity lies within the normal category and angles of bank exceeding 60° are not permitted

13. One important reason for taking off into a headwind is:

    a. To enable the aircraft to lift off at a higher speed and have a longer ground run

    b. To enable the aircraft to lift off at a higher speed and have a shorter ground run

    c. To enable the aircraft to lift off at a lower speed and have a shorter ground run

    d. To enable the aircraft to lift off at a lower speed and have a longer ground run

14. When operating from a grass runway pilots can expect:

    a. The Landing Distance Required to increase due to reduced braking efficiency

    b. The Landing Distance Required to be unaffected, especially if the grass is short

    c. The Landing Distance Required to decrease if the grass is wet

    d. The Landing Distance Required to reduce due to increased friction from the grass

15. Taking off from sea level you intend to climb to 6,000 feet. Assuming a standard atmosphere and that you adopt the recommended climb speed, from the table below determine:

    i) the time it will take to reach 6,000 feet

    ii) the fuel used from start up; and

    iii) the distance flown during the climb

TIME, FUEL AND DISTANCE TO CLIMB
AT 2390 POUNDS
CONDITIONS: FLAPS UP, FULL THROTTLE, STANDARD TEMPERATURE

PRESSURE ALTITUDE FT	TEMP °C	CLIMB SPEED KIAS	RATE OF CLIMB FPM	FROM SEA LEVEL		
				TIME IN MINUTES	FUEL USED GAL	DISTANCE NM
SEA LEVEL	15	82	760	0	0.0	0
1000	13	81	710	1	0.5	2
2000	11	80	670	3	0.9	4
3000	9	79	630	4	1.3	6
4000	7	78	595	6	1.7	9
5000	5	77	550	8	2	12
6000	3	76	505	10	2.4	15
7000	1	75	475	14	2.9	19
8000	-1	74	420	18	3.4	23
9000	-3	73	380	22	4	25
10000	-5	72	315	25	5.4	30

NOTES:
1. Add 1.3 gallons of fuel for engine start, taxi and take-off
2. Increase time, fuel and distance by 10% for each 10°C above standard temperature
3. Distances based on zero wind
4. Mixture leaned above 3,000 feet for maximum RPM

    a. i) 10   ii) 2.4   iii) 15

    b. i) 14   ii) 2.9   iii) 19

    c. i) 10   ii) 3.7   iii) 15

    d. i) 10   ii) 2.4   iii) 19

16. An aircraft is cruising at 4,000 feet, the pilot decides to climb to 8,000 feet. From the table above determine:

i)   the time it will take to reach 8,000 feet

ii)   the fuel used; and

iii)   the distance flown during the climb

Assume a standard atmosphere and that the recommended climb speed is used.

  a.   i) 18   ii) 3.4   iii) 23

  b.   i) 12   ii) 1.7   iii) 14

  c.   i) 6   ii) 1.7   iii) 9

  d.   i) 10   ii) 2.4   iii) 15

17. Carburettor icing is more likely:

  a.   At high level

  b.   In the winter

  c.   At high power settings, when the throttle butterfly is fully open

  d.   At low power settings, when the throttle butterfly is only partially open

18. Any ice accretion on an aircraft's wing will cause:

  a.   Weight and drag to increase, and lift to reduce significantly

  b.   Weight, drag and lift to reduce significantly

  c.   Weight and drag to decrease, but lift to increase

  d.   Weight and drag to increase, but will have no effect on the lift generated

19. Compared with gliding in still air, gliding with a tailwind will ... (i)... the distance covered over the ground and will ...(ii)... the rate of descent:

  a.   i) reduce   ii) reduce

  b.   i) increase   ii) not change

  c.   i) increase   ii) increase

  d.   i) not change   ii) reduce

PTO for question 20.

20. Using the table on the below. For an aircraft weighing 2300 pounds flying at a pressure altitude of 7,000 feet with an OAT of minus 10°C the maximum rate of climb will be:

 a.   460 fpm
 b.   490 fpm
 c.   430 fpm
 d.   510 fpm

MAXIMUM RATE OF CLIMB AT 2300 POUNDS

CONDITIONS:
Full Throttle
Flaps Up

PRESSURE ALTITUDE FEET	CLIMB SPEED KIAS	RATE OF CLIMB - FPM			
		-20°C	0°C	20°C	40°C
S.L.	80	840	780	720	630
2000	79	740	675	615	555
4000	77	675	595	535	475
6000	75	550	485	435	380
8000	73	440	375	320	260
10000	71	330	275	220	165
12000	69	210	145	- - -	- - -

INTENTIONALLY BLANK

	A	B	C	D
1.				X
2.		X		
3.	X			
4.	X			
5.				X
6.		X		
7.				X
8.		X		
9.		X		
10.			X	
11.	X			
12.				X
13.			X	
14.	X			
15			X	
16.		X		
17.				X
18.	X			
19.		X		
20.	X			

CORRECT ANSWERS: PERCENTAGES					
15	16	17	18	19	20
75%	80%	85%	90%	95%	100%

1. **(Answer: D)** A runway with a uphill slope will decrease the landing distance and will increase the take off distance as the aircraft will accelerate faster. A 2% up slope will increase the take off distance by 10%, a factor of 1.1. AIC 127/2006 (Pink 110)

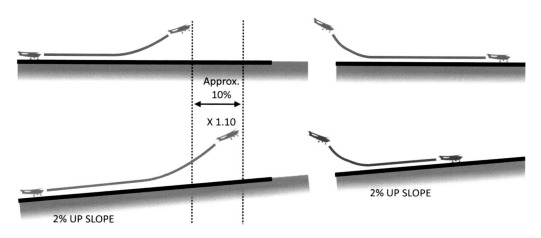

FURTHER READING: APM VOLUME 4, SECTION 4, CHAPTER 31 – TAKE-OFF & LANDING PERFORMANCE

2. **(Answer: B)** 189 l

The first thing to do is find out the weight available to use for fuel:
2400 - (1600 + 320 + 30 + 140 + 10) = 300 lbs

Max Take off Mass Authorised 2400 lbs
Max Landing Mass Authorised 2300 lbs
CG limits: 18 to 22 inches aft of datum

Item	Mass (lb)	Arm	Moment (lb In)
Basic Mass	1600	+27	+43,200
Pilot & Front Passenger	320	−6	−1,920
Oil (SG 0.8)	30	−17	−510
Rear Passengers	140	+24	+3,360
Baggage	10	+42	+420
Fuel (SG 0.72)	300	+20	
TOTAL	**2400**		

Next we need to find out how many litres weigh 300 lb. There are two ways to tackle these problems either mathematically or using the CRP Flight Computer.

Mathematically: 300 lb ÷ 2.2 = 136.4 kg
We are told in the loading graph that the specific gravity of the fuel is 0.72. A specific gravity of 0.72 means that Avgas weighs only 0.72 times as much as an equal volume of water. One litre of water weighs 1 kg, so one litre of Avgas weighs 0.72 kg.
136.4 ÷ 0.72 = 189.3 lt

CRP-1: Set the 300 on the rotating inner scale below 72 on the Imperial specific gravity scale. Below the km-m-ltr index on the fixed outer scale, we can read off 190 on the inner scale. Obviously this is jolly close to 189 lt!

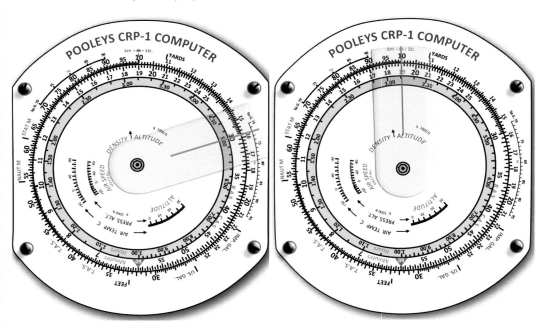

FURTHER READING: APM VOLUME 4, SECTION 4, CHAPTER 33 – MASS & BALANCE

3. **(Answer: A)** CG position on departure: 21.08 inches aft of datum.

CG position on landing: 21.18 inches aft of datum

Load sheet for departure:

Item	Mass (lb)	Arm	Moment (lb In)
Basic Mass	1600	+27	+43,200
Pilot & Front Passenger	320	−6	−1,920
Oil (SG 0.8)	30	−17	−510
Rear Passengers	140	+24	+3,360
Baggage	10	+42	+420
Fuel (SG 0.72)	250	+20	+5,000
TOTAL	**2400**		**+49,550**

CG position on departure $= \dfrac{49550}{2,350} = 21.08$ inches aft of datum

Load sheet for landing:

Item	Mass (lb)	Arm	Moment (lb In)
Basic Mass	1600	+27	+43,200
Pilot & Front Passenger	320	−6	−1,920
Oil (SG 0.8)	30	−17	−510
Rear Passengers	140	+24	+3,360
Baggage	10	+42	+420
Fuel (SG 0.72)	50	+20	+1,000
TOTAL	**2150**		**+45,550**

CG position on landing $= \dfrac{45,550}{2,150} = 21.18$ inches aft of datum

4. **(Answer: A)** 86.31 inches aft of datum

    Given:
    Aircraft planned take-off weight: 2300 lb
    CG on departure: 85.75 inches aft of datum
    Fuel burn: 300 lb (position 82 inches aft of datum)

    Method:
    1. Find the aircraft moment on departure = weight X moment arm = 2300 x 85.75 = 197,225 lb in
    2. Find the moment arm of the fuel used: 300 x 82 = 24,600 lb in
    3. Find the landing moment by subtracting the fuel used moment from the departure moment: 197,225 − 24,600 = 172,625 lb in
    4. Find the landing weight: 2300 − 300 = 2000 lb
    5. Finally divide the landing moment by the landing weight to find the CG position on landing: 172,625 ÷ 2000 = 86.31 inches aft of datum

    FURTHER READING: APM VOLUME 4, SECTION 4, CHAPTER 33 — MASS & BALANCE

5. **(Answer: D)** 85.125 inches aft of datum

    Given:
    Aircraft planned take-off weight: 2200 lb
    CG on departure: 84.75 inches aft of datum
    Fuel burn: 200 lb (position 81 inches aft of datum)

    Method:
    1. Find the aircraft moment on departure = weight X moment arm = 2200 x 84.75 = 186,450 lb in
    2. Find the moment arm of the fuel used: 200 x 81 = 16,200 lb in
    3. Find the landing moment by subtracting the fuel used moment from the departure moment: 186,450 − 16,200 = 170,250 lb in
    4. Find the landing weight: 2200 − 200 = 2000 lb
    5. Finally divide the landing moment by the landing weight to find the CG position on landing: 170,250 ÷ 2000 = 85.125 inches aft of datum

    FURTHER READING: APM VOLUME 4, SECTION 4, CHAPTER 33 — MASS & BALANCE

6. **(Answer: B)** 91.05 inches aft of datum

    Given:
    Aircraft planned take-off weight: 2300 lb
    CG on departure: 90.75 inches aft of datum
    Fuel burn: 170 lb (position 87 inches aft of datum)

    Method:
    1. Find the aircraft moment on departure = weight X moment arm = 2300 x 90.75 = 208,725 lb in
    2. Find the moment arm of the fuel used: 170 x 87 = 14,790 lb in
    3. Find the landing moment by subtracting the fuel used moment from the departure moment: 208,725 − 14,790 = 193,935 lb in
    4. Find the landing weight: 2300 − 170 = 2130 lb
    5. Finally divide the landing moment by the landing weight to find the CG position on landing: 193,935 ÷ 2130 = 91.05 inches aft of datum

    FURTHER READING: APM VOLUME 4, SECTION 4, CHAPTER 33 — MASS & BALANCE

7.   **(Answer: D)** Total moment: 179,100 lb in; CG position: 84.88 inches aft of the datum

Given:

Before refuelling aircraft weight: 1800 lbs
Total moment: 151,200 lb in.
Weight of fuel: 310 lb of fuel (position 90 inches aft of the datum)

	Weight	Moment Arm	Moment
Aircraft	1800		151,200
Fuel	310	90	27,900
TOTAL	**2110**		**179,100**

CG position = total moment ÷ total weight = 179,100 ÷ 2110 = 84.88 inches aft of the datum

FURTHER READING: APM VOLUME 4, SECTION 4, CHAPTER 33 – MASS & BALANCE

8.   **(Answer: B)** CG position: 95.56 inches aft of the datum

Given:

Before refuelling aircraft weight: 1900 lbs
Moment: 162,200 lb in.
Weight of fuel: 400 lb (position 12 ft aft of the datum)

Note the catch here, the fuel CG position is given in feet. This must be converted to inches for the calculation:
12 x 12 = 144 inches

	Weight	Moment Arm	Moment
Aircraft	1900		162,200
Fuel	400	144	57,600
TOTAL	**2300**		**219,800**

CG position = total moment ÷ total weight = 219,800 ÷ 2300 = 95.56 inches aft of the datum

FURTHER READING: APM VOLUME 4, SECTION 4, CHAPTER 33 – MASS & BALANCE

9.   **(Answer: B)** The use of flap on approach allows a steeper approach path to be flown (providing better forward vision) and a slower approach speed to be adopted.

Lift = CL ½ρV2S

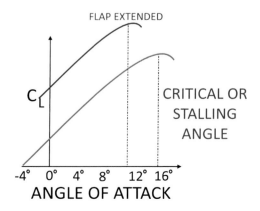

Flaps enable the lift required to oppose the aircraft's weight to be generated at a lower speed and the aircraft will stall at a lower indicated airspeed. Since the approach speed is calculated on the stalling speed in the landing configuration ($V_{AT} = V_{SO}$ x 1.3) the approach speed will be reduced.

FURTHER READING: APM VOLUME 4, SECTION 4, CHAPTER 31 – TAKE-OFF & LANDING PERFORMANCE

10. **(Answer: C)** An overweight aircraft will handle and perform badly and, if flown, may suffer structural damage.

Other effects of increased weight are:
Higher take off speed
Longer take off run
Higher stalling speed
Reduced climb performance (both rate and angle of climb)
Increased fuel consumption and so less endurance
Shorter range
Higher landing speed and longer landing distance
Reduced manoeuvrability

FURTHER READING: APM VOLUME 4, SECTION 4, CHAPTER 33 – MASS & BALANCE

11. **(Answer: A)** A low friction surface such as grass or snow increase the ground roll, as despite the increased rolling resistance of the surface brake effectiveness is reduced and this is the more significant factor.

Guide line factors:
Dry grass (under 8 inches) the landing distance will be increased by 15% (a factor of x 1.15).
Wet grass (under 8 inches) the landing distance will be increased by 35% (a factor of x 1.35).
When the grass is very short, the surface may be slippery and distances may increase by up to 60% (a factor of x 1.60)
For snow, the landing distance will be increased by 25% or more (a factor of at least x 1.25).
AIC 127/2006 (Pink 110)

FURTHER READING: APM VOLUME 4, SECTION 4, CHAPTER 31 – TAKE-OFF & LANDING PERFORMANCE

12. **(Answer: D)** The aircraft centre of gravity lies within the normal category and angles of bank exceeding 60° are not permitted.

Departure mass: 1010 kg
Total moment: 930 kg.m

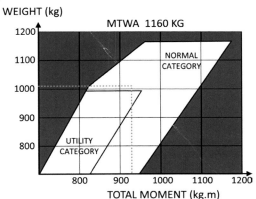

EASA Certification Specifications state:
The normal category is limited to non-aerobatic operations. Non-aerobatic operations include –
(1) Any manoeuvre incident to normal flying;
(2) Stalls (except whip stalls); and
(3) Lazy eights, chandelles and steep turns or similar manoeuvres, in which the angle of bank is not more than 60°.
The utility category is limited to any of the operations covered in the normal category; plus -
(1) Spins (if approved for the particular type of aeroplane); and
(2) Lazy eights, chandelles, and steep turns, or similar manoeuvres in which the angle of bank is more than 60° but not more than 90°.

EASA-CS 23.3 see also the UK General Aviation Safety Sense Leaflet number 9.

FURTHER READING: APM VOLUME 4, SECTION 4, CHAPTER 31 – TAKE-OFF & LANDING PERFORMANCE

13. **(Answer: C)** One important reason for taking-off into a headwind is to enable the aircraft to lift off at a lower speed and have a shorter ground run. A headwind can be considered as free airspeed towards that required to lift off; also once airborne the climb gradient relative to the ground is improved giving better obstacle clearance. A tailwind has the opposite effect; a tailwind component of 10% of the lift off speed will increase the take off distance by 20%.

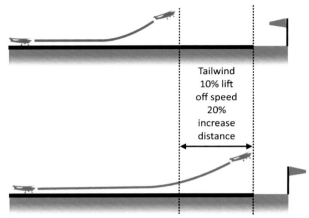

FURTHER READING: APM VOLUME 4, SECTION 4, CHAPTER 31 – TAKE-OFF & LANDING PERFORMANCE

14. **(Answer: A)** When operating from a grass runway pilots can expect the Landing Distance Required to increase due to reduced braking efficiency. (Part of graph from Safety leaflet)

FURTHER READING: APM VOLUME 4, SECTION 4, CHAPTER 31 – TAKE-OFF & LANDING PERFORMANCE

15. **(Answer: C)**
    i)   the time it will take to reach 6,000 feet = 10 minutes
    ii) the fuel used from start up = 3.7 (From the notes section do not forget to " Add 1.3 gallons of fuel for engine start, taxi and take-off")
    iii) the distance flown during the climb = 15 nm

				FROM SEA LEVEL		
PRESSURE ALTITUDE FT	TEMP °C	CLIMB SPEED KIAS	RATE OF CLIMB FPM	TIME IN MINUTES	FUEL USED GAL	DISTANCE NM
SEA LEVEL	15	82	760	0	0.0	0
1000	13	81	710	1	0.5	2
2000	11	80	670	3	0.9	4
3000	9	79	630	4	1.3	6
4000	7	78	595	6	1.7	9
5000	5	77	550	8	2	12
6000	3	76	505	**10**	**2.4**	**15**
7000	1	75	475	14	2.9	19
8000	-1	74	420	18	3.4	23
9000	-3	73	380	22	4	25
10000	-5	72	315	25	5.4	30

TIME, FUEL AND DISTANCE TO CLIMB AT 2390 POUNDS
CONDITIONS: FLAPS UP, FULL THROTTLE, STANDARD TEMPERATURE

NOTES:
1. Add 1.3 gallons of fuel for engine start, taxi and take-off
2. Increase time, fuel and distance by 10% for each 10°C above standard temperature
3. Distances based on zero wind
4. Mixture leaned above 3,000 feet for maximum RPM

FURTHER READING: APM VOLUME 4, SECTION 4, CHAPTER 31 – TAKE-OFF & LANDING PERFORMANCE

16. **(Answer: B)**

    i)   the time it will take to reach 8,000 feet = 12 minutes
    ii) the fuel used = 1.7 gallons
    iii) the distance flown during the climb = 14 nm

    The table is compiled as if the aircraft is climbing from sea level; intermediate data must be interpolated. Begin by entering the table at the level to which the aircraft will climb, 8,000 feet in this case and note the details; next obtain the values for the level from which climb is commenced, in this instance 4,000 feet and subtract them from the 8,000 feet numbers.

TIME, FUEL AND DISTANCE TO CLIMB						
AT 2390 POUNDS						
CONDITIONS: FLAPS UP, FULL THROTTLE, STANDARD TEMPERATURE						
PRESSURE ALTITUDE FT	**TEMP °C**	**CLIMB SPEED KIAS**	**RATE OF CLIMB FPM**	**FROM SEA LEVEL**		
				TIME IN MINUTES	**FUEL USED GAL**	**DISTANCE NM**
SEA LEVEL	15	82	760	0	0.0	0
1000	13	81	710	1	0.5	2
2000	11	80	670	3	0.9	4
3000	9	79	630	4	1.3	6
4000	7	78	595	6	1.7	9
5000	5	77	550	8	2	12
6000	3	76	505	10	2.4	15
7000	1	75	475	14	2.9	19
8000	-1	74	420	18	3.4	23
9000	-3	73	380	22	4	25
10000	-5	72	315	25	5.4	30

NOTES:
1. Add 1.3 gallons of fuel for engine start, taxi and take-off
2. Increase time, fuel and distance by 10% for each 10°C above standard temperature
3. Distances based on zero wind
4. Mixture leaned above 3,000 feet for maximum RPM

	Time in Minutes	**Fuel used Gal**	**Distance NM**
8,000 feet	18	3.4	23
4,000 feet	6	1.7	9
8,000 – 4,000 feet	12	1.7	14

FURTHER READING: APM VOLUME 4, SECTION 4, CHAPTER 31 – TAKE-OFF & LANDING PERFORMANCE

17. **(Answer: D)** Throttle icing: occurs when the fuel/air mix accelerates past the throttle butterfly valve leading to a temperature drop, and to the possibility of ice forming on the throttle valve. At small throttle openings the acceleration and temperature drop are at their greatest, a situation exacerbated by the fact that at small throttle openings not a great deal of ice is necessary to from a blockage. For this reason there is a greater likelihood of carburettor icing at reduced power settings.

FURTHER READING: APM VOLUME 4, SECTION 2, CHAPTER 17 – THE CARBURETTOR

18. **(Answer: A)** Ice accretion on wings adds a great deal of weight and significantly increases drag. Additionally it can drastically reduce the lift generated by a wing; this is especially true when ice forms on the upper surface.

FURTHER READING: APM VOLUME 4, SECTION 1, CHAPTER 10 – STRAIGHT & LEVEL

19. **(Answer: B)** Compared with gliding in still air, gliding with a tailwind will increase the distance covered over the ground but will not change the rate of descent.

When gliding with a tailwind, the aircraft is moving over the ground at its TAS plus the speed of the moving airmass, it will therefore travel further over the ground than in still air. The glide angle is considered relative to the airmass and is thus unaffected by the wind. The aircraft has the same TAS, the same nose attitude, the same angle of attack and the same rate of descent whether flying in still air or a head/tailwind. Rate of descent refers to time, so the aircraft will remain airborne for the same amount of time regardless of wind, but will travel further in that time with a tailwind.

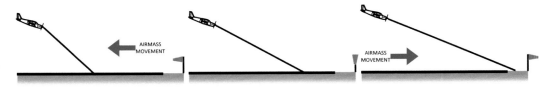

FURTHER READING: APM VOLUME 4, SECTION 1, CHAPTER 12 — DESCENDING

20. **(Answer: A)** 460 fpm

PRESSURE ALTITUDE FEET	CLIMB SPEED KIAS	RATE OF CLIMB - FPM			
		-20°C	0°C	20°C	40°C
S.L.	80	840	780	720	630
2000	79	740	675	615	555
4000	77	675	595	535	475
6000	75	550	485	435	380
8000	73	440	375	320	260
10000	71	330	275	220	165
12000	69	210	145	- - -	- - -

MAXIMUM RATE OF CLIMB AT 2300 POUNDS
CONDITIONS: Full Throttle, Flaps Up

This is a two-stage process. First we must find the values at 7,000 feet for both -20°C and at 0°C and then interpolate between our results.

In the performance table pressure altitudes are given at 2,000 ft intervals, thus to find the maximum rate of climb at 7,000 feet with an OAT of -20°C and 0°C we must interpolate between the figures given.

The 7,000 ft rate of climb at -20°C = (550 + 440) ÷ 2 = 490 fpm
The 7,000 ft rate of climb at -0°C = (485 + 375) ÷ 2 = 430 fpm

To find the 7,000 ft rate of climb at -10°C interpolate between these answers. As the temperature is exactly half way between the values we have: (490 + 430) ÷ 2 = 460 fpm

FURTHER READING: APM VOLUME 4, SECTION 1, CHAPTER 11 — CLIMBING

END OF EXPLANATIONS PAPER 3

1. Given:

Aircraft planned take-off weight: 2450 lb
CG on departure: 88.7 inches aft of datum
Fuel burn: 240 lb (position 85 inches aft of datum)

On landing what is the calculated CG position?
- **a.** 107.5 inches aft of datum
- **b.** 89.1 inches aft of datum
- **c.** 73.2 inches aft of datum
- **d.** 80.37 inches aft of datum

2. Before refuelling an aircraft weighs 2100 lbs, the total moment was 170,800 lb in. 350 lb of fuel are then loaded having an arm 86.7 inches aft of the datum. The aircraft's CG will now be:
- **a.** 80.26 inches aft of datum
- **b.** 57.32 inches aft of datum
- **c.** 95.7 inches aft of datum
- **d.** 82.1 inches aft of datum

3. When compared to still air conditions, with a strong tailwind the best range speed will be:
- **a.** Slower
- **b.** Faster
- **c.** Higher or lower, depending upon the cruise altitude
- **d.** Unaffected

4. You have planned an early morning departure. The aircraft requires a measured take off distance to a height of 50 feet of 350 m and you calculated the TODR as 512 m using a 2% upslope runway, a 1900 lb aircraft, and an OAT of +10°C.

Poor visibility prevents your planned early departure, and by the time departure is possible the OAT is +20°C and your friend weighing 190lb can now make the trip. What is the new TODR?
- **a.** 614 m
- **b.** 676 m
- **c.** 898 m
- **d.** 563 m

5. Using small flap settings (up to 20°) on take-off will:
- **a.** Provide a large increase in lift and a large increase in drag. The take-off run will not be affected
- **b.** Provide a small increase in lift and a large increase in drag. The take-off run will be reduced
- **c.** Provide a large increase in lift and a small increase in drag. The take-off run will be reduced
- **d.** Provide a small increase in lift and a small increase in drag. The take-off run will be reduced

6. V_2, the take-off safety speed is:
- **a.** V_{S1} x 1.2 and should provide at least a 20% margin above the stalling speed
- **b.** V_{S1} x 1.33 and should provide at least a 33% margin above the stalling speed
- **c.** V_{NO} x 1.2 and should provide at least a 20% margin above the stalling speed
- **d.** V_{NE} x 1.33 and should provide at least a 33% margin above the stalling speed

7. An increase in gross weight will ... (i) ... the speed at which the aircraft rotates and ... (ii) ... the take-off safety speed:

a.   i) increase   ii) increase
b.   i) increase   ii) decrease
c.   i) decrease   ii) increase
d.   i) decrease   ii) decrease

8. Using the table below determine the i) % BHP ii) TAS and iii) fuel burn for an aircraft cruising in an atmosphere 20°C above standard at 6,000 feet with a constant RPM of 2100.

a.   i) 69 ii) 117 iii) 9.0
b.   i) 61 ii) 107 iii) 8.1
c.   i) 65 ii) 109 iii) 8.5
d.   i) 59 ii) 105 iii) 7.9

9. Using the table below determine the i) % BHP ii) TAS and iii) fuel burn for an aircraft cruising in a standard atmosphere at 4,000 feet with a constant RPM of 2200.

a.   i) 69 ii) 115 iii) 9.0
b.   i) 68 ii) 114 iii) 8.9
c.   i) 72 ii) 115 iii) 9.4
d.   i) 77 ii) 117 iii) 9.9

CRUISE PERFORMANCE

CONDITIONS: 2500 POUNDS, RECOMMENDED LEAN MIXTURE AT ALL ALTITUDES

PRESSURE ALTITUDE	RPM	20°C BELOW STANDARD TEMPERATURE			STANDARD TEMPERATURE			20°C ABOVE STANDARD TEMPERATURE		
		% BHP	KTAS	GPH	% BHP	KTAS	GPH	% BHP	KTAS	GPH
2000	2300	- - -	- - -	- - -	81	119	10.3	76	120	9.8
	2250	81	116	10.4	76	116	9.8	72	115	9.3
	2150	71	111	9.2	67	110	8.8	64	109	8.4
	2050	63	105	8.3	60	103	7.9	57	101	7.7
	1950	56	100	7.5	53	95	7.2	52	93	7.1
4000	2350	- - -	- - -	- - -	81	121	10.4	77	121	9.9
	2300	82	119	10.5	77	118	9.9	72	118	9.4
	2200	77	117	9.9	72	115	9.4	68	114	8.9
	2100	68	110	8.9	64	109	8.4	61	107	8.1
	2000	60	104	8	57	102	7.7	55	99	7.5
	1900	54	96	7.3	52	94	7.1	51	97	6.9
6000	2400	- - -	- - -	- - -	82	124	10.5	77	123	9.9
	2350	82	121	10.5	77	121	9.9	72	120	9.4
	2300	78	119	10	73	118	9.4	69	117	9
	2200	73	116	9.4	69	115	9	66	113	8.6
	2100	65	109	8.5	62	108	8.2	59	105	7.9
	2000	58	102	7.7	55	100	7.5	54	97	7.3

10. Whilst flying in the vicinity of a broken layer of cumulus cloud, you notice ice building on the wings. The most appropriate action to take is to:

a. Climb above the cloud
b. Continue your current flight path, but closely monitor the situation
c. Descend into warmer air, or make a 180° turn
d. Climb into warmer air

11. Overloading an aircraft will:

a. Improve both the range and endurance
b. Slow acceleration and increase the take-off run
c. Reduce the rate of climb, but will not affect the maximum operating altitude
d. Increase the aircraft's manoeuvrability

12. Advice is contained in a Safety Sense Leaflet regarding the effect of runway surface on distances required. It states that when landing on dry grass (less than 8 inches long) will ... (i) ... the landing distance by ... (ii) ...; landing on very short wet grass will ... (iii) ... the landing distance by up to ... (iv) ...:

a. i) increase ii) 10% iii) increase iv) 30%
b. i) increase ii) 20% iii) decrease iv) 50%
c. i) decrease ii) 10% iii) decrease iv) 30%
d. i) increase ii) 20% iii) increase iv) 60%

13. If an aircraft is loaded so that the CG is at the forward limit, the aircraft will:

a. Experience a decrease in longitudinal stability
b. Be very stable in pitch and require high elevator forces during the flare
c. Experience a reduction in the stalling speed
d. Be very stable in pitch and require only small elevator forces during the flare

14. If an aircraft is loaded so that the CG is at the aft limit, the aircraft will:

a. Be more stable in pitch
b. Have a higher stalling speed
c. Require a reduction in elevator force required during the flare
d. Require an increase in elevator force required during the flare

15. With all tanks full an aircraft holds 380 litres of fuel. If the specific gravity (SG) of the fuel is 0.72, what is the approximate weight of the fuel in pounds?

a. 602 lbs
b. 274 lbs
c. 158 lbs
d. 699 lbs

MAXIMUM RATE OF CLIMB AT 2300 POUNDS						
CONDITIONS: Full Throttle, Flaps Up						
PRESSURE ALTITUDE FEET	CLIMB SPEED KIAS	RATE OF CLIMB - FPM				
		-20°C	0°C	20°C	40°C	
S.L.	80	840	780	720	630	
2000	79	740	675	615	555	
4000	77	675	595	535	475	
6000	75	550	485	435	380	
8000	73	430	375	320	260	
10000	71	330	275	220	165	
12000	69	210	145	- - -	- - -	

16. Use the table above to determine the following:

For an aircraft weighing 2300 pounds flying at a pressure altitude of 2,000 feet with an OAT of minus 10°C the maximum rate of climb will be:

a. 635 fpm
b. 810 fpm
c. 642 fpm
d. 705 fpm

17. If the aircraft below is fuelled with 200 lbs of fuel, of which 120 lbs will be burned during the flight what is the CG position on departure and on landing?

Max Take off Mass Authorised 2400 lbs
Max Landing Mass Authorised 2300 lbs
CG limits: 18 to 22 inches aft of datum

Item	Mass (lb)	Arm	Moment (lb In)
Basic Mass	1600	+27	+43,200
Pilot & Front Passenger	320	−6	−1,920
Oil (SG 0.8)	30	−17	−510
Rear Passengers	140	+24	+3,360
Baggage	10	+42	+420
Fuel (SG 0.72)	200	+20	
TOTAL			

a. CG position on departure: 22.2 CG position on landing: 22.1
b. CG position on departure: 21.10 CG position on landing: 21.17
c. CG position on departure: 20.5 CG position on landing: 27.9
d. CG position on departure: 21.18 CG position on landing: 21.68

18. What is the gradient of a 2500 ft runway which has threshold elevations of 355 and 460 feet?

a. 4.2 %
b. 32.6 %
c. 6.5 %
d. 3.7 %

19. Refer to the Take Off Performance Graph to answer the following:

Given:

OAT: +30°C
Pressure Altitude: 3,000 feet
Aircraft Weight: 2900 lbs
Surface Wind: 30 knots Headwind

What is the approximate take off distance required to reach a screen height of 50ft?

a.   1000 feet
b.   1540 feet
c.   990 feet
d.   1380 feet

TAKE OFF DISTANCE - FLAPS UP

ASSOCIATED CONDITIONS
POWER .... TAKE-OFF POWER SET BEFORE BRAKE RELEASE
MIXTURE .... FULL RICH
FLAPS .... UP
LANDING GEAR .... RETRACT AFTER POSITIVE CLIMB ESTABLISHED
COWL FLAPS .... OPEN
RUNWAY .... PAVED, LEVEL AND DRY SURFACE

20. The best rate of climb:

a.   Gains the greatest amount of height in the shortest time
b.   Gains the greatest amount of height in the shortest distance over the ground
c.   Gains the greatest amount of height with the greatest horizontal speed
d.   Gains the greatest amount of height in the greatest distance over the ground

END OF FLIGHT PERFORMANCE AND PLANNING PAPER 4

	A	B	C	D
1.		X		
2.				X
3.	X			
4.		X		
5.			X	
6.	X			
7.	X			
8.				X
9.			X	
10.			X	
11.		X		
12.				X
13.		X		
14.			X	
15	X			
16.				X
17.		X		
18.	X			
19.				X
20.	X			

CORRECT ANSWERS: PERCENTAGES					
15	16	17	18	19	20
75%	80%	85%	90%	95%	100%

FLIGHT PERFORMANCE AND PLANNING

1. **(Answer: B)** 89.1 inches aft of datum

Given:

Aircraft planned take-off weight: 2450 lb
CG on departure: 88.7 inches aft of datum
Fuel burn: 240 lb (position 85 inches aft of datum)

Method:

1. Find the aircraft moment on departure = weight X moment arm = 2450 x 88.7 = 217,315 lb in
2. Find the moment arm of the fuel used: 240 x 85 = 20,400 lb in
3. Find the landing moment by subtracting the fuel used moment from the departure moment:
   217,315 − 20,400 = 196,915 lb in
4. Find the landing weight: 2450 − 240 = 2210 lb
5. Finally divide the landing moment by the landing weight to find the CG position on landing:
   196,915 ÷ 2210 = 89.1 inches aft of datum

FURTHER READING: APM VOLUME 4, SECTION 4, CHAPTER 33 — MASS & BALANCE

2. **(Answer: D)** 82.1 inches aft of the datum

Before refuelling, an aircraft weighs 2100 lbs, the total moment was 170,800 lb in. 350 lb of fuel are then loaded having an arm 86.7 inches aft of the datum. The aircraft's CG will now be:

Given:

Before refuelling aircraft weight: 2100 lbs
Moment: 170,800 lb in.
Weight of fuel: 350 lb (position 86.7 inches aft of the datum)

	Weight	Moment Arm	Moment
Aircraft	2100		170,800
Fuel	350	86.7	30,345
TOTAL	**2450**		**201,145**

CG position= total moment ÷ total weight = 201,145 ÷ 2450 = 82.1 inches aft of the datum

FURTHER READING: APM VOLUME 4, SECTION 4, CHAPTER 33 — MASS & BALANCE

3. **(Answer: A)** When compared to still air conditions, with a strong tailwind to help progress, the best range speed will be slower. As the tailwind is assisting progress over the ground, we can reduce the power and consequently the fuel consumption and still achieve the best range. In headwind conditions the best range speed is faster than the still air best range, as even though fuel consumption will be greater flying faster will give the headwind less time to act on the aircraft.

FURTHER READING: APM VOLUME 4, SECTION 4, CHAPTER 32 — ENROUTE PERFORMANCE

4. **(Answer: B)** Any factors applied to the calculated take-off distance must be multiplied.

Originally the TODR: 350 x 1.1 (2% upslope) x 1.33 (safety factor) = 512 m
The new TODR for the later departure: 350 x 1.1 (2% upslope) x 1.2 (10% increase weight) x 1.1 (10°C increase temp) x 1.33 (safety factor) = 676 m

FURTHER READING: APM VOLUME 4, SECTION 4, CHAPTER 31 — TAKE-OFF & LANDING PERFORMANCE

5.   **(Answer: C)** Using small flap settings (up to 20°) on take-off will provide a large increase in lift and a small increase in drag. The take-off run will be reduced.

Take-off flap refers to relatively small flap settings up to around 20°. Extra lift is generated by altering the effective camber of the wing, this happens with a fairly small drag penalty. The result is a slower lift off speed, a slower take-off safety speed and a shorter take-off ground run required. However, once airborne flap will reduce both the rate and angle of climb so the take-off distance (the distance to reach 50 ft) may not be significantly reduced.

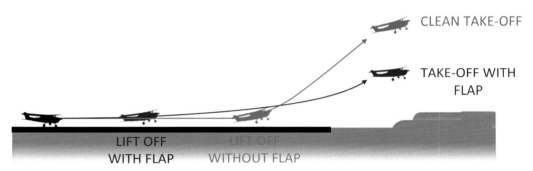

Landing flap is the term used to describe flap settings between 20° and 40°. These settings create large amounts of drag with relatively little increase in lift.

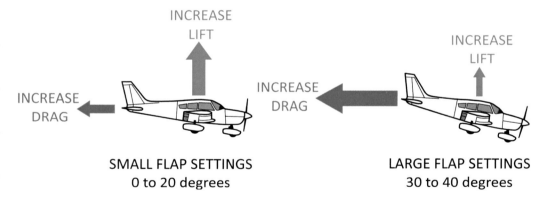

FURTHER READING: APM VOLUME 4, SECTION 4, CHAPTER 31 – TAKE-OFF & LANDING PERFORMANCE

6.   **(Answer: A)** V_2, the take-off safety speed is V_{S1} x 1.2 and should provide at least a 20% margin above the stalling speed.

FURTHER READING: APM VOLUME 4, SECTION 4, CHAPTER 31 – TAKE-OFF & LANDING PERFORMANCE

7.   **(Answer: A)** An increase in gross weight will increase the speed at which the aircraft rotates and increase the take-off safety speed.

The lift generated by a wing is proportional to speed for a given angle of attack, should the aircraft's weight increase more lift is required to balance the extra weight and this must be generated by increasing speed. The speed at which the aircraft lifts off will therefore be higher. A heavier aircraft will also have a higher stalling speed.

The Take-Off Safety Speed is a function of V_{S1}, so, if the stall speed is higher the TOSS must also be higher. The take-off safety speed is V_{S1} x 1.2 and should provide at least a 20% margin above the stalling speed. The Take-Off Safety Speed is the speed that is assumed in performance calculations to be flown from lift off to a 50 ft screen height.

FURTHER READING: APM VOLUME 4, SECTION 4, CHAPTER 31 – TAKE-OFF & LANDING PERFORMANCE

8. **(Answer: D)** i) % BHP 59 ii) TAS 105 knots iii) Fuel burn 7.9 GPH

    Enter the table at the appropriate level, in this question 6,000 feet, then move along to the second column which is the RPM and select the row for 2100 RPM. Finally select the last 3 columns of data, those for ISA +20°C.

CRUISE PERFORMANCE

CONDITIONS: 2500 POUNDS, RECOMMENDED LEAN MIXTURE AT ALL ALTITUDES

PRESSURE ALTITUDE	RPM	20°C BELOW STANDARD TEMPERATURE			STANDARD TEMPERATURE			20°C ABOVE STANDARD TEMPERATURE		
		% BHP	KTAS	GPH	% BHP	KTAS	GPH	% BHP	KTAS	GPH
2000	2300	- - -	- - -	- - -	81	119	10.3	76	120	9.8
	2250	81	116	10.4	76	116	9.8	72	115	9.3
	2150	71	111	9.2	67	110	8.8	64	109	8.4
	2050	63	105	8.3	60	103	7.9	57	101	7.7
	1950	56	100	7.5	53	95	7.2	52	93	7.1
4000	2350	- - -	- - -	- - -	81	121	10.4	77	121	9.9
	2300	82	119	10.5	77	118	9.9	72	118	9.4
	2200	77	117	9.9	72	115	9.4	68	114	8.9
	2100	68	110	8.9	64	109	8.4	61	107	8.1
	2000	60	104	8	57	102	7.7	55	99	7.5
	1900	54	96	7.3	52	94	7.1	51	97	6.9
6000	2400	- - -	- - -	- - -	82	124	10.5	77	123	9.9
	2350	82	121	10.5	77	121	9.9	72	120	9.4
	2300	78	119	10	73	118	9.4	69	117	9
	2200	73	116	9.4	69	115	9	66	113	8.6
	2100	65	109	8.5	62	108	8.2	59	105	7.9
	2000	58	102	7.7	55	100	7.5	54	97	7.3

FURTHER READING: APM VOLUME 4, SECTION 4, CHAPTER 32 – ENROUTE PERFORMANCE

9. **(Answer: C)** i) 72 % BHP ii) TAS 115 knots iii) Fuel burn 9.4 GPH

CRUISE PERFORMANCE

CONDITIONS: 2500 POUNDS, RECOMMENDED LEAN MIXTURE AT ALL ALTITUDES

PRESSURE ALTITUDE	RPM	20°C BELOW STANDARD TEMPERATURE			STANDARD TEMPERATURE			20°C ABOVE STANDARD TEMPERATURE		
		% BHP	KTAS	GPH	% BHP	KTAS	GPH	% BHP	KTAS	GPH
2000	2300	- - -	- - -	- - -	81	119	10.3	76	120	9.8
	2250	81	116	10.4	76	116	9.8	72	115	9.3
	2150	71	111	9.2	67	110	8.8	64	109	8.4
	2050	63	105	8.3	60	103	7.9	57	101	7.7
	1950	56	100	7.5	53	95	7.2	52	93	7.1
4000	2350	- - -	- - -	- - -	81	121	10.4	77	121	9.9
	2300	82	119	10.5	77	118	9.9	72	118	9.4
	2200	77	117	9.9	**72**	**115**	**9.4**	68	114	8.9
	2100	68	110	8.9	64	109	8.4	61	107	8.1
	2000	60	104	8	57	102	7.7	55	99	7.5
	1900	54	96	7.3	52	94	7.1	51	97	6.9
6000	2400	- - -	- - -	- - -	82	124	10.5	77	123	9.9
	2350	82	121	10.5	77	121	9.9	72	120	9.4
	2300	78	119	10	73	118	9.4	69	117	9
	2200	73	116	9.4	69	115	9	66	113	8.6
	2100	65	109	8.5	62	108	8.2	59	105	7.9
	2000	58	102	7.7	55	100	7.5	54	97	7.3

FURTHER READING: APM VOLUME 4, SECTION 4, CHAPTER 32 – ENROUTE PERFORMANCE

10. **(Answer: C)** Whilst flying in the vicinity of a broken layer of cumulus cloud, you notice ice building on the wings. The most appropriate action to take is to descend into warmer air (if terrain permits) or reverse course to an area where you know icing conditions were not present. Ice accumulations on the wings will increase weight and disrupt laminar flow over the lift generating surfaces.

FURTHER READING: APM VOLUME 4, SECTION 1, CHAPTER 10 – STRAIGHT & LEVEL

11. **(Answer: B)** Overloading an aircraft will slow acceleration and increase the take-off run. Additionally, an overweight aircraft will handle and perform badly and, if flown, may suffer structural damage.

Other effects of increased weight are:
Higher take off speed
Longer take off run Higher stalling speed
Reduced climb performance (both rate and angle of climb)
Increased fuel consumption and so less endurance
Shorter range
Higher landing speed and longer landing distance
Reduced manoeuvrability

FURTHER READING: APM VOLUME 4, SECTION 4, CHAPTER 33 – MASS & BALANCE

12. **(Answer: D)** Landing on dry grass (less than 8 inches long) will increase the landing distance by 20%; landing on very short wet grass will increase the landing distance by up to 60%.

Extract from Safety Sense Leaflet – Aeroplane performance:

Condition	Take Off		Landing	
	INCREASE IN DISTANCE TO HEIGHT 50 FEET	FACTOR	INCREASE IN LANDING DISTANCE FROM 50 FEET	FACTOR
Dry Grass – up to 8 in	20%	1.2	20%	1.2
Wet Grass – up to 8 in	30%	1.3	30%	1.3 When the grass is very short, the surface may be slippery and distances may increase by up to 60%

Rather annoyingly the AIC relating to light aircraft performance (127/2006 Pink 110) quotes slightly different figures:

Guide line factors from Pink 110:
For dry grass (under 8 inches) the landing distance will be increased by 15% (a factor of x 1.15).
For wet grass (under 8 inches) the landing distance will be increased by 35% (a factor of x 1.35).

NOTE 1: WHEN THE GRASS IS VERY SHORT, THE SURFACE MAY BE SLIPPERY AND DISTANCES
MAY INCREASE BY UP TO 60% (A FACTOR OF X 1.60)

At least both agree on the effect of very short, wet grass! Make sure you read the question carefully to determine exactly which source you are asked to quote.

FURTHER READING: APM VOLUME 4, SECTION 4, CHAPTER 31 – TAKE-OFF & LANDING PERFORMANCE

13. **(Answer: B)** If the centre of gravity is at or close to its forward limit the aircraft's longitudinal stability is increased, i.e. it becomes more stable in pitch. This is because the tailplane has a very long moment arm (moment = force x distance).

The aircraft will feel extremely nose- heavy and resistant to changes in pitch. It is probable that the pilot may not be able to prevent the nose pitching down at low speed, for instance when landing, even with the control column fully aft.

Exceeding the forward limit may lead to:
Difficulty during rotation
Increased stall speed
Greater induced drag leading to increased fuel consumption and consequently reduced range
Difficulty in flying a stable approach
Difficulty in flaring during landing

FURTHER READING: APM VOLUME 4, SECTION 4, CHAPTER 33 – MASS & BALANCE

14. **(Answer: C)** If the centre of gravity is at or close to its aft limit the aircraft's longitudinal stability is reduced, i.e. it becomes less stable in pitch. In this case the tailplane has its minimum moment arm; hence its effectiveness is reduced. With an aft C of G, lift generated from the wing will give a nose-up pitching moment, even a slight increase in angle of attack will cause the lift to increase and a greater nose-up pitching moment to be experienced. This cycle would repeat and eventually the aircraft would become uncontrollable in pitch leading to a stall from which recovery would be doubtful.

With an aft C of G it is the aircraft's natural tendency to pitch up meaning that only very slight elevator forces will be required in the flare. The danger here would be to over pitch and stall onto the runway.

Exceeding the aft limit may lead to:
Rotating early on take off
The danger of stalling during climb
Longitudinal instability
Degraded stall recovery

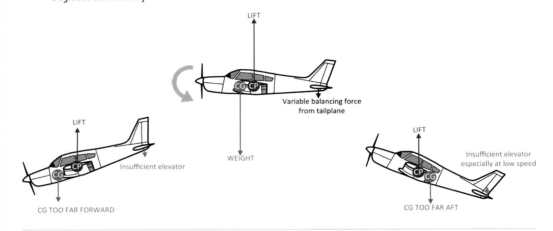

CG TOO FAR FORWARD

CG TOO FAR AFT

FURTHER READING: APM VOLUME 4, SECTION 4, CHAPTER 33 – MASS & BALANCE

15. **(Answer: A)** There are two ways to tackle these problems - either mathematically or using the Pooleys CRP-1 Flight Computer.

Mathematically: a specific gravity of 0.72 means that Avgas weighs only 0.72 times as much as an equal volume of water. One litre of water weighs 1 kg, so one litre of Avgas weighs 0.72 kg. 380 litres x 0.72 = 273.6 kgs

However we are asked for an answer in pounds:
273.6 x 2.2 = 601.9 lbs

15. ANSWER A

CRP: Set the number of litres (380) under the litres index on the fixed outer scale. Also on the fixed outer scale are two scales for specific gravity (Sp. G) one in kgs and one in lbs. Below 72 on the Imperial Sp. G scale read off approximately 600 lb on the INNER rotating scale.

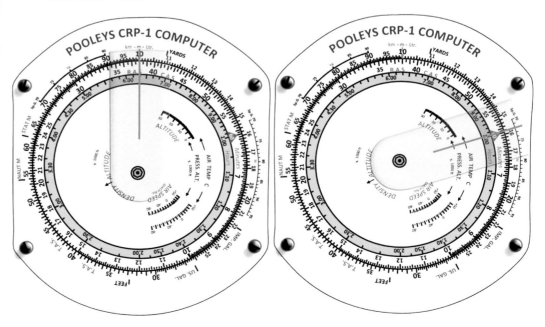

FURTHER READING: APM VOLUME 4, SECTION 4, CHAPTER 33 – MASS & BALANCE

16.   (Answer: D) 705 fpm

<table>
<tr><td colspan="6">MAXIMUM RATE OF CLIMB AT 2300 POUNDS
CONDITIONS: Full Throttle, Flaps Up</td></tr>
<tr><td rowspan="2">PRESSURE
ALTITUDE
FEET</td><td rowspan="2">CLIMB
SPEED
KIAS</td><td colspan="4">RATE OF CLIMB - FPM</td></tr>
<tr><td>-20°C</td><td>0°C</td><td>20°C</td><td>40°C</td></tr>
<tr><td>S.L.</td><td>80</td><td>840</td><td>780</td><td>720</td><td>630</td></tr>
<tr><td>2000</td><td>79</td><td>740</td><td>675</td><td>615</td><td>555</td></tr>
<tr><td>4000</td><td>77</td><td>675</td><td>595</td><td>535</td><td>475</td></tr>
<tr><td>6000</td><td>75</td><td>550</td><td>485</td><td>435</td><td>380</td></tr>
<tr><td>8000</td><td>73</td><td>430</td><td>375</td><td>320</td><td>260</td></tr>
<tr><td>10000</td><td>71</td><td>330</td><td>275</td><td>220</td><td>165</td></tr>
<tr><td>12000</td><td>69</td><td>210</td><td>145</td><td>- - -</td><td>- - -</td></tr>
</table>

In the performance table temperatures are given at 20 degree intervals. Thus to find the maximum rate of climb at 2,000 feet with an OAT of -10°C we must interpolate between the figures given.

At 2,000 feet in the 0°C column we find the maximum rate of climb is 675 fpm; in the -20°C column it is 740 fpm. To find the value for -10°C add these two values together and, as -10°C is exactly half way in between the given values, divide by 2.
675 + 740 = 1415 ÷ 2 = 707.5 fpm. The nearest answer is 705 fpm.

FURTHER READING: APM VOLUME 4, SECTION 1, CHAPTER 11 – CLIMBING

17.   (Answer: B)

CG position on departure: 21.10 inches aft of datum
CG position on landing: 21.17 inches aft of datum

Max Take off Mass Authorised 2400 lbs
Max Landing Mass Authorised 2300 lbs
CG limits: 18 to 22 inches aft of datum

Load sheet for departure:

Item	Mass (lb)	Arm	Moment (lb In)
Basic Mass	1600	+27	+43,200
Pilot & Front Passenger	320	−6	−1,920
Oil (SG 0.8)	30	−17	−510
Rear Passengers	140	+24	+3,360
Baggage	10	+42	+420
Fuel (SG 0.72)	200	+20	+4,000
TOTAL	**2,300**		**+48,550**

CG position on departure = 48,550 ÷ 2,300 = 21.10 inches aft of datum

Load sheet for landing:

Item	Mass (lb)	Arm	Moment (lb In)
Basic Mass	1600	+27	+43,200
Pilot & Front Passenger	320	−6	−1,920
Oil (SG 0.8)	30	−17	−510
Rear Passengers	140	+24	+3,360
Baggage	10	+42	+420
Fuel (SG 0.72)	80	+20	+1,600
TOTAL	**2,180**		**+46,150**

CG position on arrival = 46,150 ÷ 2,180 = 21.17 inches aft of datum

FURTHER READING: APM VOLUME 4, SECTION 4, CHAPTER 33 – MASS & BALANCE

18.   (Answer: A) 4.2%

To calculate the runway gradient:

$$\frac{\text{Higher threshold} - \text{Lower threshold}}{\text{Runway length}} \times \frac{100}{1}$$

$$\frac{460 - 355}{2500} \times \frac{100}{1} = 4.2\%$$

FURTHER READING: APM VOLUME 4, SECTION 4, CHAPTER 31 – TAKE-OFF & LANDING PERFORMANCE

19. (Answer: D) 1,380 feet

1. Enter the graph from the bottom at +30°C and draw a line vertically upwards to the actual pressure altitude, in this case 3,000 feet.
2. Draw a horizontal line to the first reference line
3. Follow the direction of the nearest "weight" lines until the take-off weight, 2900 lbs, is reached.
4. From this point draw a horizontal line to the second reference point.
5. Parallel the nearest lines representing headwind remembering to use only 50% of the reported headwind. If you are to use the full wind speed it should state this in the flight manual. In this case use 15 knots.
6. Again, draw a horizontal line this time to the third reference line.
7. Finally, follow the nearest lines to obtain the 50 ft screen height figure, 1,380 feet.

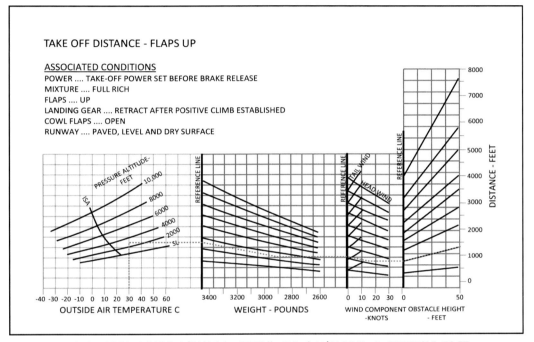

OAT: +30 PA: 3,000 ft A/C Weight: 2900 lbs Wind: H/W 30 Knots OBSTACLE: 50 FT

NOTE: TO THIS FIGURE WE SHOULD THEN ADD THE TAKE OFF SAFETY FACTOR OF 1.33, TOGETHER WITH ANY ADDITIONAL FACTORS FOR RUNWAY SURFACE, SLOPE ETC.. THAT MAY BE NECESSARY TO OBTAIN THE TAKE-OFF DISTANCE REQUIRED.

FURTHER READING: APM VOLUME 4, SECTION 4, CHAPTER 31 – TAKE-OFF & LANDING PERFORMANCE

---

20. (Answer: A) The best rate of climb is used to gain the greatest altitude in the shortest time. The greater the excess power the greater the rate of climb, hence the best rate of climb speed generally occurs near the best lift/drag ratio. The best angle of climb is used to gain the most altitude in the shortest distance travelled. Best angle depends upon excess thrust available and is usually slightly slower than the best rate of climb speed.

FURTHER READING: APM VOLUME 4, SECTION 1, CHAPTER 11 – CLIMBING

END OF EXPLANATIONS PAPER 4

INTENTIONALLY BLANK

Additional Blank Answer Sheets

INTENTIONALLY BLANK

ANSWER SHEETS

PAPER NO.				
	A	B	C	D
1				
2				
3				
4				
5				
6				
7				
8				
9				
10				
11				
12				
13				
14				
15				
16				
17				
18				
19				
20				

PAPER NO.				
	A	B	C	D
1				
2				
3				
4				
5				
6				
7				
8				
9				
10				
11				
12				
13				
14				
15				
16				
17				
18				
19				
20				

PAPER NO.				
	A	B	C	D
1				
2				
3				
4				
5				
6				
7				
8				
9				
10				
11				
12				
13				
14				
15				
16				
17				
18				
19				
20				

PAPER NO.				
	A	B	C	D
1				
2				
3				
4				
5				
6				
7				
8				
9				
10				
11				
12				
13				
14				
15				
16				
17				
18				
19				
20				

PAPER NO.				
	A	B	C	D
1				
2				
3				
4				
5				
6				
7				
8				
9				
10				
11				
12				
13				
14				
15				
16				
17				
18				
19				
20				

PAPER NO.				
	A	B	C	D
1				
2				
3				
4				
5				
6				
7				
8				
9				
10				
11				
12				
13				
14				
15				
16				
17				
18				
19				
20				

PAPER NO.				
	A	B	C	D
1				
2				
3				
4				
5				
6				
7				
8				
9				
10				
11				
12				
13				
14				
15				
16				
17				
18				
19				
20				

PAPER NO.				
	A	B	C	D
1				
2				
3				
4				
5				
6				
7				
8				
9				
10				
11				
12				
13				
14				
15				
16				
17				
18				
19				
20				

PAPER NO.				
	A	B	C	D
1				
2				
3				
4				
5				
6				
7				
8				
9				
10				
11				
12				
13				
14				
15				
16				
17				
18				
19				
20				

PAPER NO.				
	A	B	C	D
1				
2				
3				
4				
5				
6				
7				
8				
9				
10				
11				
12				
13				
14				
15				
16				
17				
18				
19				
20				

PAPER NO.				
	A	B	C	D
1				
2				
3				
4				
5				
6				
7				
8				
9				
10				
11				
12				
13				
14				
15				
16				
17				
18				
19				
20				

PAPER NO.				
	A	B	C	D
1				
2				
3				
4				
5				
6				
7				
8				
9				
10				
11				
12				
13				
14				
15				
16				
17				
18				
19				
20				